Learning Language Through Literature

THE TAN
STUDENT ACTIVITY BOOK

By

Diane Welch

and

Susan Simpson

Common Sense Press™

The *Learning Language Arts Through Literature* Series:

The Blue Book - 1st Grade Skills
The Red Book - 2nd Grade Skills
The Yellow Book - 3rd Grade Skills
The Orange Book - 4th Grade Skills
The Purple Book - 5th Grade Skills
The Tan Book - 6th Grade Skills
The Green Book - 7th Grade Skills
The Gray Book - 8th Grade Skills
The Gold Book American Literature- High School Skills
The Gold Book British Literature- High School Skills

Scripture taken from the NEW AMERICAN STANDARD BIBLE ®
©Copyright The Lockman Foundation
1960, 1962, 1963, 1968, 1971, 1972, 1973, 1975, 1977
Used by Permission.

Printed in the United States of America.

Rev 05/10
Printed 12/10
ISBN: 978-1-880892-21-3

BOOK STUDY

on
Carry On, Mr. Bowditch

Vocabulary

The following vocabulary words deal with some aspect of navigation. Look up the following words in the dictionary and write a clear definition for each word. Make sure your definition deals with navigation.

1. sextant - (Chapter 6) _____

_____

2. ship log or chip log - (Chapter 6) _____

_____

3. compass - (Chapter 12) _____

_____

4. chronometer - (Chapter 12) _____

_____

5. spyglass - (Chapter 15) _____

_____

Use the definitions of your vocabulary words to help you match each word with the correct picture.

_____   _____   _____

_____   _____

Message to the Student

Welcome to *Learning Language Arts Through Literature*! This is the *Tan Student Activity Book* where you will record your answers to the questions in the *Tan Teacher Book*.

You will enjoy learning language arts as you read good books and practice your writing skills in fun and creative ways. Remember, any skill seems difficult at first, but as you complete each day's work, you are getting better and better.

Enjoy yourself this year while *Learning Language Arts Through Literature*.

✐ Teacher's Note

This *Tan Student Activity Book* is a companion to the *Tan Teacher Book* from the series *Learning Language Arts Through Literature*. Not intended to be used independently, the complete information, material, and answer keys you need to teach are found in the *Tan Teacher Book*, also sold by Common Sense Press. Look for these and other Common Sense Press products at book stores or contact us at:

Common Sense Press
8786 Highway 21
Melrose, FL 32666
www.commonsensepress.com

Table of Contents

Enrichment
Complete the crossword puzzle using the vocabulary words.

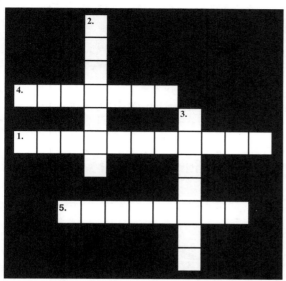

Clues

1. a timepiece used to find longitude at sea
2. an instrument used to measure the speed of a ship at sea
3. an instrument used to fix the position of a ship by measuring the distance of the sun or a star to the horizon
4. an instrument used to determine direction
5. a small telescope

Discussion Questions

Chapters 1 - 2

1. Why did Nat use the shilling he found to buy an expectation?

Chapters 3 - 4

2. Why was Nat unable to continue going to school?

Chapters 5 - 6

3. What did Nat mean when he said that he was sailing by "an ash breeze"?

Chapters 7 - 8

4. Why did Nat decide to teach himself Latin?

Chapters 9 - 10

5. Why did Nat feel he was collecting his expectation from the *Pilgrim* when he was invited to join The Salem Philosophical Library?

Chapters 11 - 12

6. How did Nat apply Elizabeth Boardman's expression about "stumbling on people's dumbness" to teaching the seamen navigation?

Chapters 13 - 14

7. Why was Nat so upset when he found a mistake in Moore's *Navigator*?

Chapters 15 - 16

   8. How did Nat handle the troublemaker, Lem Harvey, aboard the *Astrea*?

Chapters 17 - 18

   9. Who did Nat marry and why was it only for a short time?

Chapters 19 - 20

   10. What three things did Nat decide that his book of navigation would contain?

Chapters 21 - 22

   11. What honor was awarded to Nat by Harvard College and why was it so important to him?

Chapters 23 - 24

   12. Why was it so important to Nat to command a ship on a voyage?

Activities

To help you continue your enjoyment of *Carry On, Mr. Bowditch*, choose any two of the following activities: Journal Writing, Parts of a Ship, Mapping Skills.

1. Journal Writing

After completing Activity 3, *Mapping Skills*, use one of the journeys to create a journal entry as if you were Nat writing in one of his notebooks. Use a separate piece of paper to tell about the sights you would have seen on that journey. Refer to your book for the information you need.

2. Parts of a Ship

Look up the following words in a dictionary to find the part of the ship it identifies. Write the correct word or number in the space provided on the illustration of the ship (page 5).

1) rigging	6) halyard	11) hull
2) mast	7) poopdeck	12) prow
3) quarterdeck	8) stern	13) boom
4) capstan	9) bow	14) bowsprit
5) yard	10) keel	15) forecastle (also called fo'c'sle)

3. Mapping Skills

Nathaniel Bowditch takes a series of five voyages listed below. On the following map, use colored pencils to draw the paths that the ship took using different colored pencils. Use a world atlas to help you locate the various seaports.

1) **Voyage 1** - (red pencil) Left Salem and sailed across the Atlantic Ocean and around Africa to the Isle of Bourbon also known as Reunion, a French-owned island off the east coast of Africa

2) **Voyage 2** - (blue pencil) Left Salem and across the Atlantic Ocean sailed to Lisbon, Portugal, then stopped over in Funchal in the Madeira Islands (off the northwest coast of Africa), sailed around Africa and through the Indian Ocean to Manila Harbor in what is now the Philippines

3) **Voyage 3** - (green pencil) Left Salem and sailed across the Atlantic Ocean to Cadiz, Spain (a seaport in southwest Spain) and into the Mediterranean Sea to Alicante, Spain (a seaport in southeast Spain)

4) **Voyage 4** - (purple pencil) Left Boston and sailed across the Atlantic Ocean around Africa through the Indian Ocean to Batavia (now known as Djakarta, a seaport of Indonesia on the northwest coast of Java) then sailed to Manila Harbor located in what is now the Philippines

5) **Voyage 5** - (yellow pencil) Left Salem and sailed across the Atlantic Ocean, around Africa across the Indian Ocean to Sumatra, a western island of Indonesia

Journey 1

Journey 2

Journey 3

Journey 4

Journey 5

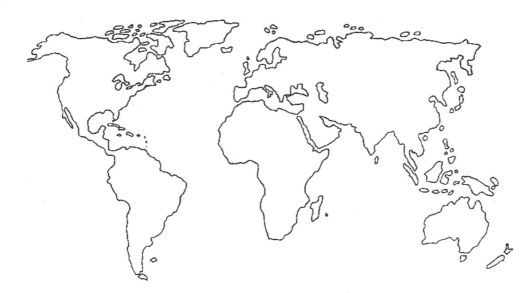

I C.A.N. Assessment

for

Carry On, Mr. Bowditch – Book Study A

After the *Book Study* is completed, check off each I C.A.N. objective with your teacher.

C   I can **complete** my work.

     I can be **creative**.

A   I can be **accurate**.

     I can do my work with a good **attitude**.

N   I can do my work **neatly**.

Blessed is the man that walketh not in the counsel of the ungodly, nor standeth in the way of sinners, nor sitteth in the seat of the scornful. But his delight is in the law of the Lord; and in his law doth he meditate day and night.

Psalm 1:1-2 (KJV)

1. a. Listen as your teacher reads the literature passage. This passage was taken from the King James Version of the Bible. The King James Version was translated in 1611. You will notice that some of the words sound differently from the way we speak today. Circle these words. The reason we no longer use these words is because English is a *living language*. A living language is a language that is spoken and used in daily communication. The language changes as new words are added, words are changed, and certain words are no longer used. For example, fifty years ago words such as videotape, modem, and internet were not a part of our language. They are words that have been added. Can you think of any other new words that have been added to our language in the last fifty years?

_____

b. Write the literature passage from dictation. Compare your copy to the passage and check for mistakes.

_____

_____

_____

_____

_____

_____

Make your own spelling list from any misspelled words or use the following list of suggested words:

counsel   meditate   delight   ungodly

_____

c. Some of the words in the verses have prefixes. A **prefix** is a letter or group of letters which come before the main part, or **root**, of the word. **Pre-** is a prefix which means *before*. Knowing the meaning of a prefix will help you understand the meaning of a word, as in *preview* which means *to view* or *show before*.

d. Another prefix in the literature passage is **un-**. Underline the word in the literature passage that has this prefix. The prefix **un-** means *not* or *release*. Knowing the meaning of this prefix, how would you define the word *ungodly*?

e. Look at the *Commonly Used Prefixes* at the back of this book. Referring to this list, write the prefixes **pre-** and **un-** in the spaces provided under the prefix heading. Add a definition and think of two word examples for each prefix. Refer to your dictionary if you need help. Keep this list available for easy reference.

Prefix	Meaning	Word Examples
pre-	before	preview, precede

Prefix	Meaning	Word Examples

2. a. In 1408 John Wycliffe was responsible for the first translation of the Latin Scriptures into the English language. The type of English used during this time period is called Middle English. Middle English was in use from the time of the Norman Conquest of 1066 to the introduction of printing in England in 1476. Many words of French origin became part of the English language at this time. Old English is the name given to the earliest English which was mostly Germanic in content. Modern English is the name given to the language from the time period extending from 1476 to present day.

   b. The origin of a word is referred to as its **etymology.** Most dictionaries give the etymology of a word, as in the sample below:

   counsel (koun's'l)n. [M.E.&OFr.]
   1. a mutual exchange of ideas, opinions, etc. . . . .

   Notice the abbreviations that appear in the brackets, [M.E.& OFr.]. These abbreviations stand for Middle English and Old French and tell us the origin of this word into the English language. Use your dictionary to look up a word from the literature passage. See if you can find the etymology for the word. (The meanings of the abbreviations used are usually found in the front section of the dictionary.)

   c. Write the list of suggested spelling words from the literature passage. If any of them are in a form that is no longer in use today, write the word that would be the modern substitute for each. Using a thesaurus, write a synonym for each word. **Synonyms** are words which have the same or similar meaning. Be sure the word you choose can be substituted for the original word in the passage without changing the meaning.

   _____

   _____

   _____

3. a. Sometimes the best way to picture the order in which events happened is by creating a timeline. Using the following information about the history of Bible translation, make a timeline. The timeline should have the earliest translation date listed starting at the far left-hand side of the timeline with dates and names continuing in correct sequence up to the most current translation, which should appear at the far right-hand side. Only the information in bold print should be written on the timeline, with the dates written at the top of the line.

   Ex: 1380s
   _____|_____

   John Wycliffe

History of Bible Translation

Information:

John Wycliffe - first English Bible translation (translated from Latin) - **1408**

Johann Gutenberg - first prints Bible - 1456

William Tyndale - English translation of the New Testament - **1525**

King James Version - the work of 50 translators; this version still in use today - **1611**

Revised Standard Version - revision of King James Version - **1946**

The Amplified Bible - a version of the Bible that gives many synonyms for words to give the most complete meaning - **1958**

New English Bible - a translation sponsored by the main British churches - **1961**

New American Standard Version - a revision of the American Revised - **1963**

Good News Bible - a translation in "common" English which people from many different ethnic backgrounds can easily understand - **1966**

The Living Bible - a paraphrase translation of the Bible - **1971**

New International Version - a translation by an international team of scholars - **1979**

Revised Authorized Version - updated translation of the King James Version - **1982**

Enrichment
Look at the letters in the word *important*. Use any of those letters to make little words. Make as many words as you can.

important

_____

_____

_____

4. a. Bible translators follow three important rules in working on a translation.
   1) Nothing must be added.
   2) Nothing must be left out.
   3) The original meaning must not be changed.

   Read the passage again. Following the three rules of Bible translation, rewrite it as we might say it today. Use some of the synonyms you listed in **2c**. If you have a Living Bible, compare your translation to this version. Are they similar?

   _____

   _____

   _____

   _____

   _____

   _____

   b. Discuss the literature passage with your teacher. How can you apply its principles to your own life?

   _____

   _____

   _____

c. Take a pretest of your spelling words. Review any words you found difficult to spell.

_____

_____

Enrichment
Unscramble these letters to make words that are synonyms.

1) igb _____   rlaeg _____

2) nyit _____   lmals _____

3) keam _____   libud _____

4) gourh _____   upbmy _____

5) vacer _____   icels _____

6) rngi _____   liems _____

a. Choose one of the following activities. Complete on separate paper.

1) Write the literature passage from dictation.

2) Read the remaining verses of Psalm 1. Tell your teacher what these verses mean to you. Rewrite verses 5 and 6 following the guidelines set forth in **4a**. Use your thesaurus to find synonyms to substitute for various words.

3) Psalm 1 compares a person who loves God's law to a well-watered tree. Draw a picture of the tree described in these verses on a blank piece of paper. Underneath the picture write two of God's laws that will help you to grow strong in your Christian walk if you obey them.

4) Choose skills from the *Review Activities* on the next page.

Review Activities

1. Add the prefix that fits the definition in parentheses.

   a. The _____liminary (*before*) practice test will help you review for the final test.

   b. The materials are _____necessary (*not*) to finish the project.

2. Use your dictionary and find the etymology of the following words.

   a. dominant _____

   b. health _____

3. Use a thesaurus to find two synonyms for each of the following words.

   a. run _____

   _____

   b. talk _____

   _____

4. Write down important events that have occurred in your life and the year these events occurred. List the events in chronological order on the timeline. Remember to keep each entry as concise as possible. Write the year above the line and the event below the line.

Nat shrugged and turned back to his bookkeeping. Even while he was still thinking of Sammy, his glance flicked down a column of figures and his fingers jotted the answer. He realized his mind was wandering. He jerked his thoughts back in line, and added the figures again. He'd been right the first time. For almost nine years now, he'd been right about figures. What would he do with the next nine years? Go on adding columns and columns of figures?

Carry On, Mr. Bowditch, by Jean Lee Latham
© 1955, renewed 1983 by Jean Lee Latham

a. Write the literature passage from dictation. Proofread and correct any errors.

b. Make a spelling list from any misspelled words or use the following list of suggested spelling words:

bookkeeping   column   thoughts   realized

c. Find the two words in the suggested spelling list that have the **/k/** sound. Note that one spells the **/k/** sound with the letter **k** and the other with the letter **c**.

> **Spelling Tip**
> To spell a word with a **/k/** sound, remember that **k** usually comes before **e** or **i**; **c** usually comes before **a**, **o**, or **u**.

d. Using this *Spelling Tip*, add the correct letter to the following words.
   Ex: <u>k</u>ite; <u>c</u>ake

   1) _____aught   6) _____ubic
   2) _____itten   7) _____eyboard
   3) _____indle   8) _____armel
   4) _____orrespond   9) _____ommission
   5) _____ettle   10) _____itchen

2. a. In the English language we identify words by placing them in one of eight different groups. These eight groups are called the **parts of speech.** The eight different parts of speech are nouns, pronouns, verbs, adjectives, adverbs, prepositions, conjunctions, and interjections. It is important to know the part each of these groups plays in a sentence and to know how to identify each of them.

   b. A **noun** is a word that names a person, place, thing, or idea. If the word names a general person, place, thing, or idea then it is a **common noun** and is not capitalized. If a noun names a specific person, place, or thing, then it is a **proper noun** and the word begins with a capital letter.
      Ex.   Proper nouns: Jake, Mt. Rushmore, Florida, etc.
            Common nouns: father, mountain, state, hope, etc.

   c. Look over the literature passage and circle all the nouns you find. Above each noun write a **C** if it is a common noun and a **P** if it is a proper noun.

3. a. **Verbs** are words that show action or a state of being. They can also link a word to the subject or help another verb.

      Ex: Jim *ran* all the way to the field. (action verb)
           We *are* here with the Brown family. (state of being verb)
           She *was* *thinking* about the answer. (helping verb)
           Jim *looks* handsome in his suit. (linking verb)

b. Often helping verbs and the main verb make up a **verb phrase**. Sometimes other words divide a verb phrase.

Ex: Many different hymns *were used* in the service.
(undivided verb phrase)

The children *were* often *divided* into groups.
Could he *have* accomplished his goals with more determination? (divided verb phrases)

Look at the list of common helping verbs.

Common Helping Verbs				
have	do	shall	would	must
has	does	will	may	can
had	did	should	might	could

All forms of the verb *be* may also be used as helping verbs.

Being Verbs			
is	are	was	were
am	been	being	

c. Underline the verbs in the literature passage. Be sure to underline both parts of a verb phrase.

d. Examine the following sentences. Identify and underline the verb phrases and circle the helping verb.
Ex: The otter (could) not <u>slide</u> down the riverbank.

1) Would you run in the race on Saturday?
2) The computer has replaced the typewriter in the business office.
3) She has almost perfected that piece of music on the piano.
4) Goats were often used to graze areas of rough terrain.
5) Could you have avoided the accident?

e. Nat knew what he could do well. Was he bragging? What are some things you can do well? Ask your teacher or friends what they think you do well. Are they the same things?

_____

_____

_____

_____

f. Review your spelling words.

4. a. A **biography** is a true story of a person's life. *Carry On, Mr. Bowditch* is a biography about Nathaniel Bowditch. Find out who he was. Look in an encyclopedia or research his name at the library. You may also want to check out this book from the library and read it. Make your notes below.

_____

_____

_____

_____

b. A **summary** is a brief description covering the main points of a certain topic. Write a short summary, about one page, of Nathaniel Bowditch's life. Make sure you include when he was born, when he died, and what he did in his life that is important to history.

_____

_____

_____

_____

_____

_____

_____

(blank lined writing space)

c. Take an oral or written spelling pretest.

Enrichment
Read each phrase below and fill in the blank with an appropriate noun.

the _____ types

the _____ hums

the _____ attacks

the _____ hustles

the _____ spins

the _____ clatters

the _____ hides

the _____ glistens

5. a. Choose one of the following activities. Complete on separate paper.

   1) Write the literature passage from dictation. Compare your copy to the model and correct any mistakes you may have made.

   2) Nat wonders what he will be doing in the future. What do you think you will be doing next year at this time? Write a few paragraphs explaining what you feel you might be doing and give reasons for your predictions.

   3) Choose skills from the *Review Activities* on the next page.

Review Activities

1. List the eight parts of speech. Give a definition for a noun and a verb.

_____

_____

_____

_____

_____

_____

_____

2. Circle the nouns and underline the verbs in the following sentences. Write a **C** above the common nouns and a **P** above the proper nouns. Be sure to underline all parts of a verb phrase.

a. The monkeys swing from branch to branch.

b. Ships will often sail through the Straits of Magellan.

c. Children should learn to enjoy good literature.

d. Mary teaches Bible to the children in her neighborhood.

e. The car swerved on the slippery road.

3. Define a biography.

_____

_____

Bambi walked under the great oak on the meadow. It sparkled like dew. It smelled of grass and flowers and moist earth, and whispered of a thousand living things. Friend Hare was there and seemed to be thinking over something important. A haughty pheasant strutted slowly by, nibbling at the grass seeds and peering cautiously in all directions. The dark, metallic blue of his neck gleamed in the sun.

Bambi by Felix Salten. Used by permission, Simon and Schuster, Inc.

1. a. Just as an artist uses paint to paint a picture, an author uses words to "paint" a word picture. Listen to the word picture the author "paints" as your teacher reads the literature passage aloud.

    b. Copy the literature passage from dictation. Proofread your copy for any mistakes.

Make a spelling list from any misspelled words or use the following suggested list:

> sparkled   whispered   gleamed
> nibbling   peering   strutted

_____

_____

_____

c. The prefix **im-** has two meanings. It can mean *not*, as in *impatient* (not patient). The prefix **im-** can also mean *into*, as in *implant*. Find the word in the literature passage with this prefix and underline it. Add this prefix to your list of prefixes you started in Lesson 1. List the prefix, its meaning, and two examples of words that contain the prefix.

d. A **suffix** is a letter or group of letters which comes at the end of the base or root of the word. While prefixes give you an understanding of the meaning of a word, suffix endings can often help in determining the part of speech of a word, whether it is a verb, adjective, etc. Notice that all the words from your suggested spelling list end in **-ing** or **-ed**. These endings do not have specific meanings, but a word ending with these suffixes is usually a verb, a word that expresses action in the sentence. All the words in your spelling list are used as verbs in the literature passage.

e. Locate the *Commonly Used Suffixes* at the back of this book. Referring to this list, write the suffix **-ed** in the space provided under the suffix heading. Write "no meaning" under *Meaning*, write "usually a verb" under *Part of Speech*, and write example words from the spelling list under *Word Examples*.

Suffix	Meaning	Part of Speech	Word Examples
-ed			

Suffix	Meaning	Part of Speech	Word Examples

You will be using this list throughout the program.

2. a. Writers often use **figurative language** to express thoughts. Sometimes it helps to produce a picture in your mind by using a comparison. When a comparison of two unrelated things is made using the words *as* or *like*, it is called a **simile**.

Ex: smooth *as* silk   *like* a raging bull
         warm *as* toast   *like* the quiet after a storm
         sweet *as* honey   *like* a newborn babe

   b. Finish the following expressions with words that create similes.

   1) as quiet as_____

   2) as light as_____

   3) as hungry as a_____

   4) sticky like_____

   5) sparkled like_____

   c. Create two of your own similes. Remember to use the words *as* or *like* when you make your comparison.

   _____

   _____

   _____

Enrichment
Draw a face for each sentence.

Examples: Bill is happy.   Jill is scared.

                              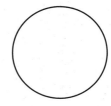

Jill is exhausted.   Bill is frustrated.   Jill is exhilarated.   Bill is terrified.

3. a. Look at your spelling list from **1b**. One way to learn how to spell a word correctly is to divide the word into syllables. A **syllable** is a division of a word that contains a vowel sound. You can usually hear each syllable as you say the word slowly. It will help to clap each time your hear a syllable division in a word. The number of times you clap is the number of syllables the word contains.

For example, the word *thinking* is divided into two syllables, *think* and **-ing** because it has two vowel sounds. The word *walked* is only one syllable because it only contains one vowel sound; the suffix **-ed** has a **/t/** sound. Write the words from your spelling list dividing the words into syllables. If you are unsure how a word should be divided, check your dictionary.

Ex: thou - sand

_____

_____

_____

_____

b. **Personification** is a form of figurative language which gives human characteristics to an idea, object, or animal. Look at the third sentence of the literature passage. How did the meadow behave like a person?

_____

c. Read the following sentence:

I heard the wind muttering through the trees.

The wind does not literally mutter, but by giving the wind human qualities, it becomes vivid and alive. What else might the wind do like a person?

_____

_____

_____

_____

_____

d. Create a sentence for each of the following phrases that uses personification. Be sure to use your imagination!

1) peeked through the clouds

2) stubbornly refused to move

3) danced among the flowers

4) swallowed him up

a. A good author desires to keep the attention of the reader, his audience. Using colorful words will capture a mood or setting, allowing the reader to feel he is experiencing the scene. Often this is done through the use of adjectives. **Adjectives** are words that describe nouns, the words which name persons, places, things, or ideas. Adjectives answer the following questions: Which one? What kind? How many? How much? Whose?

b. Look at the first sentence of the literature passage. In this sentence the adjective, *great*, describes the noun, *oak*. Locate the other adjectives used in the literature passage and circle them. Now read the passage without these words. Do you notice how it is more difficult for you to picture the scene without these words?

c. Find a picture in a book or magazine of mountains, trees, clouds, animals, or anything you might want to describe using figurative language. Write a few sentences to describe the picture using simile and/or personification. Be sure to use adjectives to help you with your description. When you are finished, read your sentences aloud. Do they "paint" a good word picture of the scene you are describing?

d. Take an oral or written spelling pretest. Remember, sounding out the syllables as you write them will help you spell them correctly.

Enrichment

Read each phrase. Look at the pictures and decide which phrase best describes them. Copy the correct phrase under each picture.

Ex:

dot, rectangle, circle

> circle, circle, triangle
> dot, rectangle, rectangle, rectangle, dot
> dot, rectangle, circle
> circle, triangle, circle

1.

2.

3.

a. Choose one of the following activities. Complete on separate paper.

1) Write the literature passage from dictation.

2) Choose a poem that offers a good descriptive image and read it to your teacher. After you have finished reading the poem, point out to the teacher any examples where the author used a simile or personification.

3) How does the literature passage make you feel? Does it sound like a place you would like to be? Rewrite the literature passage and change the mood by describing the scene differently.

Review Activities

1. Divide the following words into syllables.

   a. important ....

   b. pheasant ....

   c. direction ....

   d. meadow ....

   e. metallic ....

2. Add the correct prefix to the following words. Use the definition in the parentheses and your list of prefixes to help you choose the correct prefix.

   a. The company wants to _____port (*into*) raw material for making the product.

   b. It would be _____thinkable (*not*) to be absent from the wedding.

   c. You are listening to the _____lude (*before*) of the musical symphony.

3. Find the verbs in the following paragraph and circle them. Look for the suffixes **-ed** and **-ing** to help you identify the verbs. If there is a verb phrase, be sure to circle the full phrase.

   Mary loved to visit her cousins at the farm. The car ride seemed to take forever, but they finally arrived. "All the children are swimming in the lake," her aunt announced. "The horses are also waiting in the barn for you to see."

4. Write two similes. Be sure to use the words *like* or *as*.

   ....

   ....

   ....

   ....

Write a sentence using personification.

_____

_____

_____

_____

Underline the adjectives in the following sentences and circle the noun each adjective describes.

a. The quiet, smooth water sparkled with cheerful sunlight.

b. Soft brown eyes peeked out from under the long, silky hair.

c. The sleek, shiny car sped down the busy street.

d. A gentle breeze swept through the tall trees.

e. The bright red apple crunched as the little girl bit into it.

The Eagle

He clasps the crag with crooked hands;
Close to the sun in lonely lands,
Ringed with the azure world, he stands.

The wrinkled sea beneath him crawls;
He watches from his mountain walls,
And like a thunderbolt he falls.

Lord Alfred Tennyson

1. a. Poems are divided into groups of lines called **stanzas.** This poem is written in two three-line stanzas called **triplets.** Close your eyes and imagine the eagle as your teacher reads the poem aloud. What kind of picture did you get as you listened? Now you read it aloud.

   b. Copy the poem from dictation.

_____

_____

_____

_____

_____

_____

   Look at the last line of the first stanza. What do you think *azure* means? Often if you do not know the meaning of a word, you can guess at its meaning by using context clues. **Context clues** are the other words that appear in the line or sentence that can help you to figure out the meaning of a difficult word. Read the first stanza of the poem again. Using context clues, decide what you think the meaning of *azure* might be. Look up the word in the dictionary to check its meaning.

   c. Look in the first line of the second stanza. Locate the word with the prefix **be-**. The prefix **be-** means *on* or *away*. Find your prefix list and add this prefix to your list. Write the meaning and example words.

d. Make a spelling list from any words you misspelled in the dictation or use the following suggested spelling list:

clasps	crawls	crooked
wrinkled	ringed	watches

_____

_____

_____

Look at the word *wrinkled*. The root of this word is *wrinkle*. Notice that the silent **e** was dropped before the suffix **-ed** was added.

> **Spelling Tip**
> Words that end in a silent **e** usually drop the silent **e** before adding a suffix beginning with a vowel.

e. Add the suffixes **-ed** and **-ing** to the following words. If the word ends in a silent **e**, be sure to drop the **e** before adding the suffix beginning with a vowel.

	-ed	**-ing**
Ex: practice	practiced	practicing
1) guide		
2) escape		
3) dictate		
4) create		
5) behave		
6) believe		

2. a. In line 3 of the second stanza, what two things are said to be alike? _____
These really aren't alike in most ways, but the poet shows us one way they are similar.
The speed of the eagle falling is like the thunderbolt striking the earth. As we discussed
in Lesson 3, when the words *like* or *as* are used to make a comparison, the writer is using
a powerful writer's technique called **simile**.

b. The author also makes use of personification in this poem. Read the poem again, circling
any words that give human qualities to animals and objects. In what ways are the eagle,
lands, and sea given human qualities?

_____

_____

_____

_____

c. As well as the figurative language techniques of simile and personification, the author also
makes use of adjectives to help create a picture in the reader's mind. Underline any
adjectives you can identify in the poem.

d. Choose an animal and write a few sentences to describe it. Be sure to use adjectives and
the technique of simile or personification.

_____

_____

_____

_____

_____

_____

_____

_____

a. In "The Eagle" the last word of each line rhymes with the other words in the stanza. Words that rhyme have similar sounds in the last syllable. For example, the words *hands, lands,* and *stands* from the first stanza all rhyme because they all have the same "ands" sound in the last syllable. The rhyming of words at the end of the line is called **end rhyme**. Complete the lines of the following stanza using end rhyme.

> *Nestled in her elaborate nest*
>
> *The swallow laid her head to* _____ .
>
> *She knows she did her very* _____ .

b. The best way to write a poem with end rhyme is to write the first line of the poem about your subject and then write a list of words that rhyme with the end word that could be used in your poem. Make sure you do not choose a difficult word for your end word that would be hard to rhyme with. For example, if the first line of a poem is "He stalks the skink with spiteful eyes," then a list of words should be made that rhyme with *eyes*. It could include: spies, lies, cries.

_____

_____

_____

_____

c. Using "The Eagle" as a model, try writing a poem about the animal you chose in **2d**. Write two triplets (three-line stanzas) ending with rhyming words.

Ex:

The Cat

> *He stalks with skink with spiteful eyes,*
> *Close to the grass and dirt he lies,*
> *And like a wraith, he sneaks and spies.*
>
> *At night he curls by fire bright,*
> *And in his eyes there gleams a light*
> *Of pride's self-satisfied delight.*

d. Practice writing your suggested spelling words, dividing them into syllables.

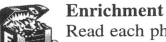

Enrichment
Read each phrase. Look at the pictures and decide which phrase best describes them.
Copy the correct phrase under each picture.

a circle on a circle	a triangle on a rectangle	a circle on a square
a square on a circle	a rectangle on a triangle	a circle on a rectangle

1.   ⬜△

_____

2.   ◎

_____

3.   ▢○

_____

4.   ⬭

_____

5.   △▭

_____

6.   ⊶◯⊷

_____

a. **Pros**   the type of writing used in a report or story. If I were to rewrite the first stanza of "The Cat" from **3c** in prose form, it would read as follows:

The cat, with a spiteful look in his eyes, stalks the skink through the grass and dirt. Like a wraith he sneaks around and spies on everything.

b. Notice the meaning of the poem has not changed by rewriting it, just the form. Read over the poem, "The Eagle." Write this poem in prose form. After you have completed rewriting the poem, read both the original version and the prose version. Which do you prefer?

c. This poem is talking about an eagle, but notice that aside from the title of the poem, the noun *eagle* is never used. Instead pronouns have been used to identify the subject. **Pronouns** are words that take the place of nouns.

PERSONAL PRONOUNS

Singular

Subjective	Possessive	Objective
I	my, mine	me
you	your, yours	you
he, she, it	his, her, hers, its	it, him, her

Plural

Subjective	Possessive	Objective
we	our, ours	us
you	your, yours	you
they	their, theirs	them

d. The noun which the pronoun takes the place of is called the **antecedent**. A pronoun must agree with the antecedent in number and gender.

Ex: *Mary, Lois, and Ginger* went to the mall where *they* shopped for new shoes. (Number - Since the antecedent is plural, the pronoun must be plural.)

John will need to take the tent, and *he* will also need *his* fishing pole. (Gender - Since the antecedent is masculine, the pronouns also need to be masculine.)

e. In the poem, "The Eagle," the antecedent is the *eagle*. Underline the pronouns that appear in the poem. (The poet chose to give the eagle a masculine pronoun.) Try reading the poem using "the eagle" wherever a pronoun appears. How does this change the effect of the poem? Do you think it would be difficult to write without pronouns? Why or why not?

f. Take an oral or written spelling pretest. Review any words you found difficult to spell.

5. a. Choose one of the following activities. Complete on separate paper.

1) Write the poem from dictation once more.

2) A poem can create a world and bring an idea to life. Other forms of art can produce the same effect in a different way. Create a picture or clay sculpture to illustrate the poem, "The Eagle."

3) Take time to enjoy reading selections of poetry aloud. Look for examples of similes and personification in the poems you read. Have your teacher (or another student) read several poems aloud without reading the titles. Try to give them new titles and compare them to the original ones.

Suggested sources for selections:

A Child's Garden of Verses by Robert Louis Stevenson
When We Were Young, Now We Are Six by A. A. Milne
Oxford Book of Poetry for Children by Edward Blishen
Favorite Poems Old and New by Helen Ferris

4) Choose skills from the *Review Activities* on the next page.

Review Activities

1. Refer to your lesson for the information to write the correct answer in the blank provided in the following sentences.

a. Poetry written in ordinary language that does not rhyme is called

   _____.

b. Words that take the place of nouns are called _____.

c. The noun the pronoun takes the place of is called the _____.

d. Poems are divided into groups of lines called _____.

e. Poems written in groupings of three lines are called _____.

f. Words that appear in a sentence that help you figure out the meaning of a word you do not know are called _____.

g. The rhyming of words at the end of a line is called _____.

2. Write a poem in triplet form with end rhyme. Write the same poem in prose form.

_____

_____

_____

_____

_____

_____

_____

_____

3. Determine from the context clues the meaning of the underlined word in the following sentences.

a. In order to avoid the traffic on the main highway, we decided to take a <u>byroad</u>.

_____

b. He was so impressed with his successful boss that he <u>emulated</u> his qualities.

_____

c. We are not sure, but he is <u>reputed</u> to be the leader of the neighborhood gang.

_____

4. Add the prefix **be-** to the following root words. Determine the definition of each word you create.

a. _____neath   _____

b. _____side   _____

c. _____siege   _____

5. Add the suffixes **-ed** and **-ing** to the following words.
   Ex: love   loved   loving

a. skate _____   _____

b. smile _____   _____

c. chase _____   _____

Read the sentences below. If the sentence contains an example of personification, write **P** in the space provided. If the sentence contains an example of a simile, write **S** in the space provided.

a. _____The birds chatted back and forth throughout the forest.

b. _____The eagle soared like a plane through the sky.

c. _____The picture was as refreshing as a garden on a spring day.

d. _____The brook laughed for joy as it cascaded over the rocks.

e. _____He ran as swiftly as a cheetah when he neared the finish of the race.

7. Underline the pronouns and draw a line to its antecedent in the following sentences.

Ex: The fledglings were ready to leave <u>their</u> nest.

a. Jim was very proud of his new car.

b. Kelly went to the swimming pool this morning, and she was going to her friend's house this afternoon.

c. The bicycle damaged its wheel on the rough terrain.

d. The Wilsons are having their house painted.

For breakfast there were pancakes, and Ma made a pancake man for each one of the children. Ma called each one in turn to bring her plate, and each could stand by the stove and watch, while with the spoonful of batter Ma put on the arms and the legs and the head. It was exciting to watch her turn the whole little man over, quickly and carefully, on a hot griddle. When it was done, she put it smoking hot on the plate.

Little House in the Big Woods by Laura Ingalls Wilder.
Used by permission, Harper and Row.

1. a. Listen as your teacher reads the literature passage. Write the passage from dictation. Compare your copy with the model, correcting the spelling and punctuation.

_____

_____

_____

_____

_____

_____

_____

_____

_____

_____

b. Using the description in the literature passage, draw a picture on a separate sheet of paper of the pancake man. Compare it to the description given. Do you feel you have drawn an accurate representation? With supervision, try cooking a pancake man.

c. The prefix **ex-** also appears in the literature passage. It means *forth* or *out*. Locate the word in the literature passage that has the prefix **ex-** . Add this prefix to your list along with the definition and word examples.

d. Choose four to six words from the literature passage for your spelling list this week or use the following suggested list:

breakfast	pancake	exciting
griddle	smoking	children

_____

_____

_____

Notice that the words *breakfast* and *pancake* are nouns that are made up of two separate complete words. These are called **compound words**.

> ### Spelling Tip
> It will be easier to remember how a compound word is spelled if you recognize the two separate words it contains. For example, **breakfast** is made up of the words **break** and **fast**. Remembering the spelling of the two separate words is less difficult than trying to remember the spelling of the whole word.

e. Divide the following compound words into separate complete words:

1) smokehouse _____

2) peanuts _____

3) pancake _____

4) gingerbread _____

5) blackboard _____

a. Underline the two words in the literature passage that have the suffix **-ly**. The suffix **-ly** usually means *like* or *manner of* and often changes words into adverbs. Add this suffix to your list. Write "usually an adverb" under the part of speech, then fill in the definition and word examples.

b. **Adverbs** are words that describe a verb, an adjective, or another adverb.
   Ex: He ran *swiftly*. - The adverb *swiftly* describes the verb *ran*.
   The garden was *very* colorful. - The adverb *very* describes the adjective *colorful*.
   She drives *too* slowly. - The adverb *too* describes the adverb *slowly*.

   Adverbs answer the following questions:

   How? When? Where? To What Extent? How Often?

   Find the two adverbs you underlined. What do they describe? What question do they answer?

   ....

   ....

   Read the sentence from the literature passage without the adve   . Notice how the adverbs help you to picture the action that is happening.

c. The best way to locate adverbs is to first find the verb in the sentence and then find any words that answer the adverb questions.
   Ex: The team screamed excitedly after they won.

   The verb in this sentence is screamed. If you then ask the question, How did they scream?, you will find the word *excitedly* answers that question.   It is an adverb describing how the team screamed.

d. Circle the verb in each of the following sentences. Then find and underline the adverb that describes that verb. Remember, the suffix **-ly** often indicates the word is an adverb. What question does the adverb answer?
   Ex: The horse (pranced) nervously.   how

   1) We went to the park yesterday. ....

   2) They are leaving quickly. ....

   3) The cats seldom fight. ....

   4) The children play outside during recess. ....

   5) The play is almost finished. ....

e. Add adverbs to the following sentences in order to better describe the action that is taking place. The word in parentheses following each sentence will tell you what question the adverb should answer.
Ex: The kitten purred <u>softly</u>. (how?)

1) The diamond sparkled _____. (*How?*)

2) We will go to church _____. (*When?*)

3) We _____ miss a meeting. (*How often?*)

4) A school of fish swam _____. (*Where?*)

5) She was _____ concerned about her grade. (*To what extent?*)

a. A group of sentences about one **main idea** is divided into paragraphs. A **paragraph** is a grouping of sentences about one specific part of the topic. The paragraph will include a sentence that expresses the main idea of the paragraph and sentences that support that main idea.

b. Read over the literature passage. Using your own words, tell your teacher what this paragraph is describing. Which sentence do you feel best expresses the main idea of the paragraph?

_____

_____

_____

_____

_____

_____

_____

This sentence is called the **topic sentence**. It is the sentence that tells what the paragraph is about. The first sentence of the paragraph is usually the topic sentence.

c. The rest of the sentences in the paragraph supports or gives more information about the topic. These are called **supporting sentences**. Supporting sentences make up the body of the paragraph. If a sentence in the paragraph does not support the main idea, it is not a supporting sentence and should not be in the paragraph. Which sentences in the literature passage are supporting sentences?

d. Each paragraph should end with a **closing sentence** that summarizes or comments on the topic of the paragraph. Identify the closing sentence in the literature passage.

e. The literature passage paragraph explains how Ma made pancake men. Choose something you know how to do and write a topic sentence for a paragraph explaining how it is done. Keep your subject simple, such as how to wash the family car, set the table, or bake a cake.

f. Think about the activity you chose and the steps you take to complete it. You might want to act it out and write the steps in order as you go. For example, to bake a cake you might write:
1) Preheat oven to 325°.
2) Grease and flour two round cake pans.
3) Mix boxed cake mix with eggs, oil, and water according to the directions on the box.
4) Pour the mixture into cake pans, place in oven, and bake for 30 minutes.
5) Take the pans out of the oven and allow them to cool.
6) Remove cakes from pans and frost.

Be sure to write your steps in the correct sequence. Don't put the batter in the cake pan before you have given instructions to grease and flour the pans.

_____

_____

_____

_____

_____

_____

_____

_____

_____

g. Review your spelling words. Remember to sound them out by syllables as you spell them. If a word is a compound word, be sure to break the word into separate words as you spell it.

a. Read the sample paragraphs below. Notice the step-by-step instructions for planting a garden.

Planting a vegetable garden is a fun project that anyone can do with a little hard work and instruction. The first step to planting a garden is to choose a site for your garden. It should be a sunny location with good, rich soil, and a source of water nearby. Then you test your soil to determine what fertilizer you need to apply. Next, plan what types of vegetables you want to plant and draw out a diagram of how you want to arrange your garden.

Be sure to run your rows north and south so more sunlight will reach the plants. Then prepare the soil by breaking up any sod and turning the soil. Also remove all woody weeds and trash from the garden plot. Rake and smooth out your planting surface. Next it is time to plant your seeds.

Use a string with stakes at each end to help you to plant a straight row. Consult your seed package for information on planting depth and spacing and follow the instruction. Attach your seed package or other identification to the stake so you will know what you have planted in that row.

Finally, keep your garden well-watered, free from weeds, and apply the proper fertilizers. Now that you have learned how to plant a vegetable garden, enjoy the harvest!

b. The topic sentence tells what the paragraphs are about. The topic sentence is often the first sentence.

Underline the topic sentence. All the other sentences must support the main idea.

Transitional words help tie thoughts together. They can also show time or order throughout the paragraphs. Some transitional words are *first*, *then*, *next*, and *finally*.

Underline the transitional words.

c. Using the steps you have listed in **3f**, write sentences on a separate piece of paper to form a paragraph. Begin with your topic sentence. All the other sentences must support the main idea. Use transitional words that show time or order throughout the paragraph such as *first*, *then*, *next*, and *finally*, but do not begin all your sentences with the same word.

d. Read your paragraph.
   Does the topic sentence tell what the paragraph is about? ....
   Are the steps in the explanation written in order? ....
   Does each sentence support the topic? ....
   Does the closing sentence summarize or comment on the topic of the paragraph? ....

e. Give your paragraph to someone and ask him to follow the directions.
   Can he understand them? ....
   Do any changes need to be made to make the directions easier to follow? ....
   Make any corrections and complete your final copy.

f. Take an oral or written spelling pretest. Review any words you had trouble spelling.

Enrichment

Read the following sentences one time. Then close the book and draw a picture on a separate sheet of paper of what you read. Reread the sentences to check your picture.

A blue car was parked on the side of the road. A tall man and a big black dog were walking down the road to the car. The man had a green bag in his hand.

a. Choose one of the following activities. Complete on separate paper.

1) Write your literature passage from dictation, paying special attention to spelling.

2) Ma took the extra time to make the pancake men because she knew it was special for the children. Think of someone in your life who takes time to do special things for you. Write a letter thanking him. A friendly letter should include a **date**, **salutation**, **body**, **closing**, and your **signature**. Follow the format below for your letter. (The words in parentheses identify the parts of the letter and are not to be written as part of the letter.)

                                                    (Date)
                                               June 30, 1996

(Salutation or Greeting - remember the comma)
Dear Susan,

(Indent) _____ *(Body)*_____

_____

_____

                                           (Closing - comma)
                                          Your friend,
                                         (Signature - no period)
                                         Kathy

---

3) Choose skills from the *Review Activities* on the next page.

Review Activities

1. Use your prefix and suffix list to fill in the correct prefix to complete the word. The definition of the prefix or suffix is in parenthesis. Check to see how many you get correct. Using context clues and prefix or suffix definitions, see if you can accurately guess the meanings of the words.

   a. I believe I _____cede you in line. (*before*)

   b. The boy grinned sly_____ at his friend with a water balloon hidden behind his back. (*like, manner of*)

   c. Mary was mirth_____ when she discovered the joke had been played on her. (*full of*)

   d. His warnings went _____heeded by the sailors. (*not*)

   e. He _____pounded upon the reasons for his belief. (*forth, from, out*)

2. Create five compound words from the following words.

wood	rain	foot	pecker	room
son	bow	grand	ball	class

   _____

   _____

   _____

3. Underline the adverbs in the following sentences. What question does the adverb answer?
   Ex: We walked <u>quickly</u> to the class.   how

   a. I will write you a letter soon. _____

   b. I could hardly see the road through the fog. _____

   c. I have always completed the assignment. _____

   d. I searched everywhere for the perfect gift. _____

   e. We must be sure to leave quietly for the early morning trip. _____

4. Read the following paragraph and underline the topic sentence. There is one sentence in the paragraph that does not support the topic sentence. Cross out that sentence.

Many animals have unique techniques for escaping from their enemies. The opossum fools its enemies by rolling over, lying very still, and pretending to be dead. The armadillo protects itself from attack by rolling itself into a tight ball with only its bony plates exposed. The armadillo feeds at night on insects, birds' eggs, roots, and fruit. When a skunk is attacked it squirts a terrible-smelling liquid from under its tail at its enemy. Many attackers are defeated by these escape techniques and move on to find easier prey.

5. Add the correct punctuation to the following letter.

June 19 1997

Dear Mary

    I really miss you, and I wish you were here with us on our family vacation. The mountains are beautiful. We have enjoyed fishing, hiking, and sightseeing. Our vacation ends next week, so I should be home soon.

Your friend

Jan

There was very little hard study done in the Temple Grammar School the week preceding the Fourth of July. For my part, my heart and brain were so full of fire-crackers, Roman-candles, rockets, pin-wheels, squibs, and gunpowder in various seductive forms, that I wonder I didn't explode under Mr. Grimshaw's very nose. I couldn't do a sum to save me. I couldn't tell, for love or money, whether Tallahassee was the capital of Tennessee or of Florida. The present and the pluperfect tenses were inextricably mixed in my memory, and I didn't know a verb from an adjective when I met one.

The Story of a Bad Boy by Thomas Bailey Aldrich.

1. a. Listen to your teacher as she reads the literature passage. Write the passage from dictation. Carefully proofread and correct any errors. Pay close attention to the words which are capitalized.

b. Is Tallahassee the capital of Tennessee or Florida? If you don't know, look in an atlas, encyclopedia, or on a map to find out.

c. Locate the word *inextricably* in the literature passage. The prefix **in-** means *not* or *into*. Try to guess the meaning of *inextricably* using prefix meaning and context clues. Check your definition with the dictionary. Add the prefix **in-** to your prefix list, along with its definition and word examples.

d. Some compound words are joined together by a hyphen. Find the compound words in the literature passage that have hyphens. Locate the one compound word in the passage that is not joined together by a hyphen. What two words make up that compound? It is hard to know whether a compound is joined together with or without a hyphen. If you are unsure of the correct way to write a compound word, check with a dictionary.

e. Make a spelling list from words you misspelled or use the following suggested list:

preceding	gunpowder	whether
memory	couldn't	didn't

Two of the suggested spelling words are contractions. **Contractions** are words formed by joining two words and leaving out one or more letters. An **apostrophe** (') shows where the letter(s) have been left out.

> ### Spelling Tip
> It will help in the spelling of contractions to remember that the apostrophe is always placed at the exact point where letters are omitted.

f. Underline the four contractions used in the paragraph. What two words does each represent?

_____

Some contractions are formed by joining a verb to the word *not*, while others are formed by joining a pronoun and verb. Write the following words as contractions. Be sure to place the apostrophe in the correct position.
Ex: could not - couldn't

1) did not _____

2) have not _____

3) she will _____

4) let us _____

5) we have _____

2. a. In **1d**, we used the apostrophe in contractions to show where letter(s) had been omitted. An apostrophe can also be used to show possession. The possessive form of a singular noun is made when an apostrophe s (**'s**) is added to the noun. This is called a **singular possessive noun**.
Ex: the horse belonging to Joanna - Joanna's horse

Locate an example of a singular possessive noun in the literature passage.

b. The plural possessive form of a noun is formed by placing the apostrophe after ending s. If a plural noun is irregular and does not end in **s**, then an apostrophe s (**'s**) is used to form the possessive. This is called a **plural possessive noun**.
Ex: the room belonging to the girls - girls' room
        the cars belonging to the men - men's cars

Write each of the following nouns as a singular and plural possessive. Remember, if the plural of the noun is irregular, then an apostrophe s (**'s**) is used to form the plural possessive.

Noun	Singular Possessive	Plural Possessive
Ex: dog	dog's	dogs'

1) kitten _____

2) teacher _____

3) mouse _____

4) girl _____

5) goose _____

c. Read the literature passage once more. Locate the adverbs used in the literature passage and circle them. Remember, adverbs answer the questions: Where? When? How? How often? To what extent? Since adverbs describe verbs most of the time, first find the verb, then ask the questions that adverbs answer. The word **not** is a frequently used adverb. It is often in the contraction form, **n't**. Notice how the author's use of adverbs helps to convey a mood of excitement.

d. Have you ever been so excited over an upcoming event you couldn't concentrate on anything? Share about the event with your teacher or other students.

3. a. Reread the literature passage paying special attention to the capitalization. Capitalization is used in three main ways:

1) to indicate the beginning of a sentence
2) to help the reader quickly identify proper names and titles
3) to show respect, such as references to God and the Bible

Although there are many specific capitalization rules, most rules fall under one of the three main categories listed above. The one rule that does not fall under one of these categories is the capitalization of the letter **i** when it is used as a word. The letter **i** is always capitalized when it is used as the word *I*.

b. Circle all the words in the paragraph that begin with a capital letter. Write each of the words under the correct category which the capitalization rule would fall under. The category for showing respect has been omitted since there are no references to God in the literature passage. The first one is done for you as an example.

Beginning of Sentence	Proper Name	Title
There		

c. Pretend you are this boy's friend. Briefly write a few sentences explaining to him the difference between a verb and an adjective. Refer to the definitions for a verb and an adjective in Lessons 2 and 3 if you need help.

_____

_____

_____

_____

d. Review your spelling words.

Enrichment
Letter Search

L	M	N	O	P
Q	R	S	T	U
V	W	X	Y	Z
A	B	C	D	E

1. Start at N. Go south 2 places, west 2 places and north 1 place. What letter are you on now? _____

2. Start at S. Go north 1 place, west 2 places, south 3 places and east 2 places. What letter are you on now? _____

3. Start at E. Go west 4 places, north 1 place, east 2 places and north 1 place. What letter are you on now? _____

a. The boy in the literature passage describes his excitement concerning a holiday. What is your favorite holiday? Today you are going to write a paragraph describing your favorite holiday.

b. Before you begin writing your paragraph, it is a good idea to think about what you want to write and organize your thoughts. One of the best methods for doing this is to use a "circle word picture."

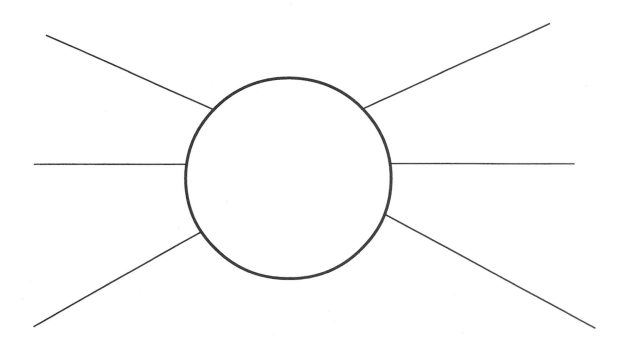

c. Look at the following circle word picture about the Fourth of July as it was described in the literature passage. After you have reviewed the example, choose your favorite holiday and write it in the center circle of the diagram. Now brainstorm. Why do you like the holiday? What special things happen? What makes it special? Put your ideas on the lines extending from the center circle.

little study
fire-crackers

squibs, gunpowder
Fourth of
July
Roman-candles

pin-wheels
rockets

d. Look over your completed diagram. Begin writing your paragraph by starting with a good topic sentence. All the other sentences you write should tell about and support the topic sentence. Then end your paragraph with a closing sentence. Be sure to use adjectives and adverbs to help convey your excitement about the holiday.

e. Look over your paragraph for any mistakes in punctuation, spelling, and capitalization. Once you are satisfied, write the paragraph neatly for your teacher to review.

f. Take an oral or written spelling pretest.

Enrichment
You are going on a trip around the world. Use an atlas or other reference materials to find a city or attraction that begins with the first letter of each letter in the phrase, "Around The World." Example: **A** - Amsterdam **R** - Rotunda in Washington, D.C.

A _____

R _____

O _____

U _____

N _____

D _____

T _____

H _____

E _____

W _____

O _____

R _____

L _____

D _____

5. a. Choose one of the following activities. Complete on separate paper.

1) Write the literature passage from dictation.

2) A caricature is a cartoon type drawing used to stretch the imagination. Can you envision this boy with his heart and brain full of firecrackers, Roman-candles, etc. right under his teacher's nose? Close your eyes and think how this would look. Draw a caricature of this scene on a blank piece of paper. You don't have to be an artist to draw a caricature. There's no right or wrong way. Draw it the way you "see" it. Have fun!

3) Choose skills from the *Review Activities* on the next page.

Review Activities

1. Look in your dictionary and find three words with the prefix **in-**. How does the prefix **in-** change the meaning of the root word?

   _____

   _____

   _____

   _____

2. Write the contractions for the following words.

   a. should not _____

   b. she will _____

   c. are not _____

   d. they have _____

   e. we would _____

3. Identify the compound words in the following sentences and add hyphens.

   a. I have saved forty five dollars.

   b. Jim is his brother in law and good friend.

   c. Being the youngest, she always wore hand me downs.

   d. She was the runner up in the contest.

4. Write each of the following expressions as a possessive.
   Ex: the earrings of the girl - the girl's earrings

a. the tails of the dogs ....

b. leaves of the trees ....

c. prints of the deer ....

d. the cars belonging to the ladies ....

e. the motorcycle belonging to Larry ....

5. The following paragraph is written without capitalization. Circle the words that need to be capitalized and explain why.

> our trip to washington, d.c. was so exciting. there was so much there to see and do. the first stop on our tour was the lincoln memorial. made out of white colorado-yule marble, the memorial is similar in shape to the greek parthenon. it took over six years to complete and was dedicated on memorial day, may 30, 1922. abraham lincoln's statue is located in the center of the memorial and the gettysburg address is etched in marble on the south wall.

6. Choose another topic of your choice. Draw a circle word picture and brainstorm, writing down your ideas on the lines extending from the main circle. Write a paragraph about your topic using the ideas you have written down.

Assessment 1
(Lessons 1 - 6)

1. A simile is a form of figurative language. It compares two different things using the words *like* or *as*. Find the simile in the following sentence:

    The invaders struck like a lightning bolt.

2. Using the words *as* or *like*, write a simile.

    _____

    _____

3. Personification is a form of figurative language. It gives a thing or idea human characteristics. What is the personification used in the following sentence:

    The sun sighed as it set in the west.

    _____

4. Give an example of personification about the wind.

    _____

    _____

5. a. What is the prefix in the word *ungodly*? _____

   b. What is the suffix? _____

6. Write a word with the suffix **-ful**. _____

7. Write a word with the prefix **ex-**. _____

8. Tell your teacher or write what an adjective does.

    _____

    _____

9. Read the following poem and rewrite it in prose.

Who Has Seen the Wind?

Who has seen the wind?
Neither I nor you:
But when the leaves hang trembling
The wind is passing thro'.

Who has seen the wind?
Neither you nor I:
But when the trees bow down their heads
The wind is passing by.

by Christina Rossetti

_____

_____

_____

_____

_____

_____

_____

10. Look at the literature passage in Lesson 5. What is the topic sentence?

_____

_____

_____

11. Write the following words as contractions.

a. he is _____

b. they are _____

c. we will _____

Rewrite the following holidays using correct punctuation.

a. columbus day _____

b. fourth of july _____

c. new year's day _____

Use your thesaurus to find three synonyms for each of the following words.

a. good _____

b. say _____

c. nice _____

d. cold _____

Complete the following sentences by adding the correct ending to the adjectives.

a. You are tall_____ than he.

b. Which of the three boys is the strong_____?

c. Bring me the long_____ of the two ropes.

d. I know which of the two children is the young_____.

e. Which of the four rooms is the warm_____?

BOOK STUDY

on

The Bronze Bow

Vocabulary

Find each of the following words in the chapters indicated and use context clues to decide the meaning of each word. Then, look up each word in the dictionary and write a definition.

1) synagogue - (Chapter 1)

_____

_____

2) Rabbi - (Chapter 1)

_____

_____

3) Zealot - (Chapter 1)

_____

_____

4) Sabbath - (Chapter 3)

_____

_____

5) mezuzah (Chapter 24)

_____

_____

Enrichment

Find the vocabulary words in the Word Search Puzzle.

```
c r s y n a g o g u e
s z i r y r e a l e e
y e l a n i o o g v v
s a b b a t h i u d a
i l o b o b t l p p c
g o o i m e z u z a h
t t w a v l o t z m i
```

Choose the correct word from the words listed above to complete the following sentences.

6) The _____ was teaching from the book of Genesis and discussing the law.

7) He touched the _____ at the doorway as he entered their home.

8) All work must be finished before the _____ begins.

9) We must meet at the _____ for worship.

10) Simon is known as a _____ because he is determined to rid his city of the Romans.

Discussion Questions

1. The **conflict** of a story is the problem that triggers the action. There are five basic types of conflict:

1) **Man versus Man** - problems between characters in the story
2) **Man versus Society** - problems with society
3) **Man versus Himself** - problems with himself
4) **Man versus Nature** - problems with natural happenings in nature
5) **Man versus Fate (God)** - problems with strange or unbelievable coincidences

What is the type of conflict in *The Bronze Bow*?

2. The theme of a story is the statement about life which the writer is trying to get across to the reader. It is sometimes called "the moral of the story." What would you say the theme is of *The Bronze Bow*?

3. What character do you most identify with in the book? Why?

4. At the end of the story Daniel doesn't follow Jesus but walks across the street to the Roman soldier. In what way does this show how Daniel has changed?

5. Discuss with your teacher the meaning of the words *traitor*, *rebel*, and *patriot*. Could one person be viewed by different people as each one of these? Was Rosh a rebel or a patriot?

6. *"It's just that I don't want to face Jesus with a lie. I couldn't bear the way his eyes would look at me."*

   "If he understood the reason he wouldn't blame you."

   "Yes, I think he would," she said thoughtfully. "I think that for Jesus a lie is impossible, no matter what the reason."

   "In war a lie is a weapon," said Daniel. "We have to use what weapons we have. Even Jesus must see that."

   What do you think Jesus would think about Daniel's conclusion about lying?

7. *"Rosh is no bandit," he said. "When he robs it is for a good purpose."*

   "So, I've heard. Rob the rich to feed the poor. I'll be glad to see the poor that gets one penny of what he took last night."

   "There may be more important needs," said Daniel.

   Is there ever a good reason for stealing? Would it make a difference if the poor did receive what Rosh's band had stolen?

8. Who did Daniel think was his enemy? Who did Jesus say was Daniel's enemy? Why?

9. Discuss Daniel's reaction to discovering Marcus had been visiting his sister? Do you think he was justified? Can you understand why he felt the way he did? What reaction did it cause in Leah?

10. As the story ends, both Daniel and Leah have greatly changed. In what ways do you think their lives will be different now? In what ways will things still be the same?

Activities

The following activities are intended to help you explore Daniel's world and better understand his experience. Choose one or two activities to complete your study. Complete on separate paper.

1. Stories can be set in many different places and times. Read about the world at the time Daniel lived. You may use your history book, an encyclopedia, or books from the library that will give you a picture of the times.

2. The setting of this story is Galilee at the time of Christ. Find a map of the area and locate the places mentioned in the story such as Capernaum, Tiberias, Jerusalem, etc.

3. Whenever an author chooses to write a fictional work that includes Jesus, he must treat the subject carefully. Do you think Mrs. Speare's portrayal of Jesus accurate to His character? Use passages from the book to support your argument.

4. Daniel was trained as a blacksmith. Research this skill. Are there still blacksmiths today?

5. In chapter 15, the author recounts the story of Jairus and his daughter. Read the account as recorded in Scripture (Luke 8:40-56). Do they agree? What information did the author add?

6. What do you think it was like to be a Roman soldier during this time? Research and write a short report.

7. One of the most compelling characters in the book is Samson. Although not much is told of him, his example of loyalty to Daniel is very moving. Using information provided, and filling in the missing details using your imagination, write a story around Samson.

8. Read *Calico Captive* and *The Witch of Blackbird Pond*.

I C.A.N. Assessment

for

The Bronze Bow - Book Study B

After the *Book Study* is completed, check off each I C.A.N. objective with your teacher.

C I can **complete** my work.

___ I can be **creative**.

A I can be **accurate**.

___ I can do my work with a good **attitude**.

N I can do my work **neatly**.

After that they went on till they came among tall beech trees and Trufflehunter called out, "Pattertwig! Pattertwig! Pattertwig!" and almost at once, bounding down from branch to branch till he was just above their heads, came the most magnificent red squirrel that Caspian had ever seen. It was far bigger than the ordinary dumb squirrels which he had sometimes seen in the castle gardens. Indeed it was nearly the size of a terrier and the moment you looked in its face you saw that it could talk. Indeed the difficulty was to get it to stop talking for, like all squirrels, it was a chatterer.

Prince Caspian by C.S. Lewis.
Used by permission, Wm. Collins & Sons, Inc.

1. a. Copy the literature passage from dictation. Proofread and correct any errors.

b. Find the word *indeed* in the literature passage. What prefix does this word contain?
_____ You know from Lesson 6 that the prefix **in-** means *not* or *into*. The root word is *deed*. The root or base of a word can be free or bound. A root word that is **free** is a word that can stand by itself, such as deed. If the root is not a word by itself, then the root is said to be **bound**. For example, the root in the word *presume* is *sume*. Since there is no such word in the English language, the root is considered bound.

c. Find the word *almost* in the literature passage. This word has the prefix **al-** which means *to* or *towards*. Look at the root or base part of the word. Is it free or bound? _____
Add the prefix **al-** to your list and be sure to write the definition and word examples.

d. Unlike the prefix, the suffix is always added to an existing word. The suffix **-er** means *one who* or *that which*. The suffix **-er** usually changes the word into a noun or adjective. Find the words *bigger* and *chatterer* in the literature passage. Identify whether the word is an adjective or noun from the way it is used in the sentence. Add the suffix **-er** to your list of suffixes and write the definition along with word examples.   Under the part of speech section include the information, noun or adjective.

e. Make a list of spelling words from any words you misspelled or use the following suggested list:

bigger	chatterer	ordinary
sometimes	difficulty	magnificent

_____

_____

_____

Look over the suggested spelling list. The word bigger has the suffix **-er**. The root of this word is *big*. When a one-syllable word ends with a short vowel and a consonant, double the last consonant before adding a suffix beginning with a vowel. Therefore, when the suffix **-er** is added to the word big, the **g** is doubled, forming the word *bigger*.

Spelling Tip
When a one-syllable word ends with a short vowel and a consonant, the final consonant must be doubled before adding a suffix beginning with a vowel.

f. Add suffixes to the following words. The first one is done for you as an example:

Root Word	Add Suffix	New Word
swim	-ing	swimming
a. mop	-ed	
b. bat	-er	
c. get	-ing	
d. run	-er	
e. dig	-ing	

2. a. Adjectives are words that describe nouns. Adjectives often show how one person or thing compares to another. There are three degrees of comparison in adjectives: positive, comparative, and superlative.

b. Circle the word in the first sentence of the literature passage that describes the beech trees. This is an adjective in the **positive form**. It only describes the noun; it does not compare the noun to anything else.
Ex: Joan is tall. (positive form)

c. Find the phrases that describe Pattertwig. Underline the word that compares the size of the squirrel with other squirrels. When comparing two objects or people, the suffix **-er** is added to most one-syllable adjectives and many two-syllable adjectives. Use the word *more* with adjectives of three or more syllables. This is the **comparative form** of an adjective.
Ex: Joan is taller than Mary. (comparative form)
        The berries are more plentiful on this bush. (comparative form)

d. When three or more objects or people are being compared, the suffix **-est** is added to most one-syllable adjectives and many two-syllable adjectives. Use the word *most* with adjectives of three or more syllables. This is the **superlative form** of the adjective.
Ex: Joan is the tallest of all the girls. (superlative form)
        She is the most cooperative student in class.   (superlative form)

Find the example in the literature passage where a superlative form is used to describe Pattertwig.

e. The comparative and superlative forms of some adjectives are formed irregularly. The most commonly used forms of irregular comparisons are listed below:

Positive	**Comparative**	**Superlative**
good, well	better	best
much, many	more	most
bad, ill	worse	worst
far	farther, further	farthest, furthest

f. Fill in the following chart with the comparative and superlative forms of each of the positive forms of adjectives listed below. The first one is done for you as an example. Watch for irregular forms.

Positive	**Comparative**	**Superlative**
small	smaller	smallest
1) wise		
2) dangerous		
3) bad		
4) fast		
5) good		

g. Read the literature passage once more. Draw a sketch or describe what you think Pattertwig looks like.

a. In this story the animals talk and have very distinct personalities. Mr. Lewis describes the squirrels as "chatterers." Think about other stories you have read in which animals have personalities. As we learned in Lesson 3, anytime an animal or object is given human qualities, the writing technique of personification is being used.

b. Choose four of the animals listed below and decide what personality traits would best suit them. List words beside each name that you feel would describe that animal.

bear   deer   lion   dog   mouse
tiger   cat   eagle   horse   dolphin
an animal of your choice

Ex: horse: stubborn, intelligent

_____

_____

_____

_____

c. Next choose two of the animals you wrote personality traits for and write one or two sentences about each animal describing the animal in a way that gives him at least one of the personality traits you chose.
Ex: horse - Lucky shook his head angrily at Vanessa when he found no treat in her pocket. Then, like a spoiled child, he refused to cooperate.

_____

_____

_____

_____

_____

_____

d. Practice writing your spelling words, sounding out the words by syllables.

Enrichment
Write two words beginning with each letter for each category.

	A	C	D
Food			
Games			
Boy's names			
Street names			

4. a. Stories often contain parts in which the characters are speaking to one another. This is called **dialogue**. Dialogue is used to help the story seem more real and alive. Whenever dialogue is used, the actual words spoken by the characters in the story are called **direct quotations**. Direct quotations are surrounded by **quotation marks** (" ")to set them apart. Examine the literature passage and underline the direct quotation. Note that a comma precedes the direct quotation in the literature passage. When writing direct quotations, follow these rules.

   b. Look over the quotation rules on the next page. Add correct punctuation to the following sentences. Be sure to enclose all direct quotations with quotation marks and capitalize the first word of a direct quotation.

   Ex: Jean said we cannot all fit in the car

   Jean said, "We cannot all fit in the car."

   1) The ringmaster cried welcome to the circus

   2) There are many formulas used in solving this equation the teacher announced

   3) Is there only one doughnut left asked Sue

   4) Touchdown yelled the announcer

   5) Did Mrs. Scott say "Matthew cannot go"

Quotation Rules

Direct Quotations

1. Be sure to capitalize the first word of a direct quotation.

2. When the speech tag comes before the direct quotation, place a comma before the direct quotation.

   Ex: Jim asked, "Can you come with us tonight?"

3. When the speech tag comes after the direct quotations, place the punctuation after the direct quotation inside the closing quotation marks.

   Ex: "We will go to the movies together," announced Sarah.
   "When does the movie start?" asked Tim.
   "You went without me!" gasped Luke.

4. Whenever punctuation is a part of the direct quotation, it appears inside the quotation marks. Punctuation goes outside the closing quotation mark if it applies to the whole sentence instead of just the direct quotation.

   Ex: The team exclaimed, "We will win this game!"
   (punctuation is part of the direct quotation)

   Who said, "Give me liberty or give me death"?
   (punctuation applies to the whole sentence)

5. When writing dialogue be sure to indent and start a new paragraph each time the speaker changes.

6. When direct quotation is more than one sentence and is not divided, then quotation marks should be used at the beginning of the quote and the end of the quote. Quotation marks should not enclose each sentence separately.

7. In a split quotation, the second part of the direct quotation does <u>not</u> begin with a capital letter.

   Ex: "Yesterday," said Amy, "we went to the beach."

c. Write a short conversation between the two animals you described in **3b** and **c**. The conversation should reflect the personality traits you have assigned to each animal. Be sure to set off each speaker's words with quotation marks, and follow the rules for direct quotations. When writing your conversation, indent and begin a new paragraph each time the speaker changes.

_____

_____

_____

_____

_____

_____

_____

_____

_____

d. Take an oral or written spelling pretest.

5. a. Choose one of the following activities. Complete on separate paper.

   1) Take the literature passage from dictation paying careful attention to spelling and punctuation.

   2) Examine your work from **4c** and make any edits. Use your thesaurus to improve your writing by substituting synonyms that add more description. For example, instead of saying the dog said, substitute a more descriptive word such as exclaimed, growled, or questioned. When you have done your best and are pleased with your work, make a neat copy to give to your teacher.

   3) Choose skills from the *Review Activities* on the next page.

Review Activities

Add the suffix to each of the following words. Be sure to double the last consonant if it is necessary.
Ex: sit + er = <u>sitter</u>

a. clap + ing   ....

b. trot + ed   ....

c. train + er   ....

d. sad + est   ....

e. lean + ing   ....

Using your list of prefixes and suffixes, add the prefix or suffix that is indicated by the definition in parentheses. In the space following the prefixes, indicate whether the root is bound or free.
Ex: <u>in</u> stead (*not or into*) <u>free</u>

a. ....caution (*before*) ....

b. ....cove (*to, towards*) ....

c. ....definite (*not*) ....

d. paint........... (*one who, that which*) ....

e. rest........... (*full of*) ....

Underline the correct adjective in the following sentences.
Ex: Mary can finish her math problems (<u>*quicker*</u>, *quickest*) than Samantha.

a. Of the two athletes, Mary is (*faster, fastest*).

b. In our family Matthew is the (*taller, tallest*).

c. Why is this dress (*more expensive, expensiver*) than the other one?

d. This butterfly is the (*most beautiful, beautifullest*) of them all.

e. This storm is (*badder, worse*) than the one we had earlier.

4. Write two sentences describing a tree using personification.

_____

_____

_____

5. Add the correct punctuation mark in the following sentences.

   a. How long does it take a caterpillar to become a butterfly Jim asked

   b. His teacher replied Once the caterpillar forms a pupa it takes about two weeks for the transformation to be complete

   c. That's amazing declared Martha

   d. Dan commented I once saw a butterfly emerge from its pupa. It looked rather wet and crumpled at first

   e. Blood pumping from the abdomen into the veins causes the wings to unfold, and when they are dry, the butterfly is able to fly away remarked his teacher

Jesus closed the book and gave it back to the attendant. The waiting congregation seemed to surge forward and to hold its breath. Again that voice made the blood leap in Daniel's veins.

"I say to you, the time is fulfilled, and the kingdom of God is at hand. Repent, and believe."

Now! Daniel leaned forward. Tell us that the moment has come! Tell us what to do! Longing swelled unbearably in his throat.

But Jesus went on speaking quietly. A rippling murmur passed across the crowd. Others too waited for the word that was not spoken. What had the man meant? He had said liberty for the oppressed. Why didn't he call them to arms against the oppressor? Repent, he said now. Repent. As though that could rid them of the Romans. Disappointed and puzzled, Daniel leaned back. The fire that had leaped up in him died down. The man's voice had been like a trumpet call. Yet where did the call lead?

The Bronze Bow by Elizabeth George Speare.
Used by permission Houghton Mifflin.

a. Read the literature passage. Good biblical fiction, while adding details, will remain true to what the Bible teaches. Can you find an account in Scripture that could be the setting for this passage? Where would you begin looking?

_____

_____

b. How did Daniel feel as he listened to Jesus? _____

_____

Why was he disappointed? _____

_____

What does it mean to repent? _____

_____

_____

_____

c. Write the literature passage from dictation. Be sure to use quotation marks to punctuate the direct quotation. Notice how the writer has identified the speaker as Jesus in the text few sentences prior to the actual quotation instead of directly prior or directly after. This method allows to text to flow more smoothly and still leaves no question as to who is speaking.

d. Look at the word *repent* in the literature passage. The prefix **re-** means *back* or *again*. Is the root of this word bound or free? Add this prefix to your list. Be sure to write the definition and word examples.

e. Make a list of spelling words from any words you misspelled in the dictation or use the following suggested list:

quietly	believe	died
veins	oppressed	oppressor

Spelling Tip

It is easy to confuse the **ie** with the **ei** letter combination. The letter comination **ie** is used in most words; **ei** is used after the letter **c** and in words that make the long /ā/ sound.

i before **e** except after **c**, and in words that say /ā/ as **neighbor** and **weigh**.

f. Write **ie** or **ei** in the following words.

1) sl_____gh   6) fr_____nd
2) rec_____ve   7) ch_____f
3) sh_____ld   8) y_____ld
4) fr_____ght   9) v_____n
5) bel_____ve   10) conc_____ve

g. Two of the words from the suggested spelling list have the same root or base word. What is the root? _____ Knowing the root of a word will help you remember how to spell it.

2. a. Remember that a simile compares two unlike things using the words *like* or *as*. Find the simile in this paragraph and underline it. What two things are being compared?

    _____

b. A **sentence** expresses a complete thought and has two parts. The part which tells who or what the sentence is about is called the **complete subject**. The other part of the sentence which tells what the subject is or does and is called the **complete predicate**. Most sentences can be divided between the complete subject and the complete predicate.
    Ex: The family / enjoys the amusement park.
          Mary Anne / is my friend.

c. Very often the subject comes at the beginning of the sentence, but not always. The subject always has a noun as its focal point. The predicate always has a verb as its focal point telling what the subject is or what action the subject is doing. It is usually easier to locate the predicate of the sentence first. Read the following sentence.

    The runner raced across the finish line.

Now ask yourself the following questions to help locate the subject and predicate of the sentence.

1) What action is taking place? _____

2) Who or what is doing the action? _____

The answer to the first question is the predicate of the sentence, and the answer to the second is the subject.

d. It is a little harder to find the subject in a sentence which asks a question. Try putting the question in statement form.

Ex: What had the man meant?

Make it into a statement: The man had meant *what*.
By doing this you put the subject in front of the verb, making it easier to find.

e. Look at the first three sentences in the last paragraph of the literature passage. Draw a line dividing the complete subject from the complete predicate as in **2b**. Be sure to first locate the predicate and then find the subject.

> But Jesus went on speaking quietly.
> A rippling murmur passed across the crowd.
> Others too waited for the word that was not spoken.

f. Every sentence has to have a subject and predicate to be complete. A sentence that does not contain both parts or does not express a complete thought is called a **fragment**. A writer should always be careful to only use complete sentences in his writing.
Ex: Going to the store. (fragment - subject missing)
   Mary is going to the store. (complete sentence)

   My brother and his friend. (fragment - predicate missing)
   My brother and his friend went with us. (complete sentence)

   While we were at the beach. (fragment - incomplete thought)
   While we were at the beach we found a starfish. (complete sentence)

g. Read the following sentences. If the sentence is a complete sentence, write **C** in front of the sentence. If it is a fragment, write **F** in front of it, and rewrite the sentence to add whatever is necessary to make it a complete sentence.

_____1) Going to the mall.
_____2) The butterfly flew from flower to flower.
_____3) The sixth grade class at church.
_____4) As we were climbing up the mountain.
_____5) When he realized his error.

3. a. There are four types of sentences, each expressing a different purpose.

> ### Sentence Types
>
> 1) A **declarative sentence** makes a statement and ends with a period.
>   Ex: Chickens are a type of bird found on most farms.
>
> 2) An **interrogative sentence** asks a question and ends with a question mark.
>   Ex: Who is coming skating with us?
>
> 3) An **imperative sentence** gives a command or makes a request. They often contain the understood subject *you*. An imperative sentence ends with a period or exclamation mark.
>   Ex: Come over here now!
>   Please put these books back on the shelf.
>
> 4) **An exclamatory** sentence expresses strong emotion or surprise and ends with an exclamation point.
>   Ex: What a noise those dogs make!
>   You scared me!

b. Notice that in imperative sentences the subject is often said to be understood. This means that although the subject is not stated, the sentence is understood to have the subject *you*. Read the following sentence.

   Close the door.

   Who is directed to close the door? The understood subject *you* is the one being directed to close the door.

c. There are four imperative sentences in the literature passage. Locate these sentences and circle them. *Who* is the understood subject.

d. Look at the literature passage and find an example of a declarative sentence and an interrogative sentence. Check with your teacher to make sure you are correct.

   _____

   _____

   _____

e. Practice writing your spelling words, sounding them out by syllables. Remember to apply your spelling rule to help you in writing **ie** in the correct order.

Enrichment
Read each list of words. Four of the words are in the same category and one is not. List the one that does not fit in the list.
Example: bicycle wagon sled car truck
          sled - a sled does not have wheels and all the other items do

1) television table radio vcr computer _____

2) puppy kitten piglet fawn cow _____

3) pie brownie broccoli ice cream candy _____

4) raccoon weasel beaver shark woodchuck _____

5) pencil pen crayon paper marker _____

6) shoes hat book pants shirt _____

7) snow refrigerator freezer air conditioner oven _____

Now, make three lists of your own and ask someone to find the word that doesn't fit.

_____

_____

_____

a. In **3a** you learned there are four types of sentences: declarative, interrogative, imperative, and exclamatory. Read each of the following sentences and decide if they are declarative (**D**), interrogative (**I**), imperative (**Imp**), or exclamatory (**E**). Fill in the blanks and add the correct punctuation at the end of each sentence.
Ex: _I_   Where are you going?

____ 1) Be sure to wash the dishes
____ 2) How beautiful the stars are
____ 3) There is a great variety of life in a rainforest
____ 4) Where will you be going this evening
____ 5) The races will begin this evening at dusk
____ 6) Who will be cooking dinner tonight
____ 7) Go to your room right now
____ 8) What a surprise to see you
____ 9) What is the agenda for tonight's meeting
____ 10) Northern lights are a beautiful sight to see

b. Read the literature passage again. Write a short paragraph explaining to Daniel what you think Jesus meant as He spoke.

_____

_____

_____

_____

_____

_____

_____

c. Take an oral or written spelling pretest. Review any words you have trouble with.

_____

_____

_____

Enrichment
Read each list of words. Write each word under the correct category.

	Living Thing	Nonliving Thing
Ex: tree wind rock ocean dog fish	tree, dog, fish	wind, rock, ocean

	Sky	Ground
clouds flowers moon dirt rocks stars		

	Hot	Cold
radiator flame freezer summer snowflake ice cream		

raccoon cow goat
chicken squirrel
woodchuck

<u>Forest Animals</u>   <u>Farm Animals</u>

ship submarine truck
car bus sailboat

<u>Land Vehicles</u>   <u>Water Vehicles</u>

soda   hot chocolate
milk   orange juice
coffee   hot tea

<u>Hot Drinks</u>   <u>Cold Drinks</u>

building stand car
believe whisper shelf

<u>Nouns</u>   <u>Verbs</u>

Now, make up three lists and categories of your own.

a. Choose one of the following activities. Complete on separate paper.

1) Write the literature passage from dictation paying special attention to spelling and punctuation.

2) Choose skills from the *Review Activities* on the next page.

Review Activities

1. Add the prefix **re-** to the following words. How does the prefix change the meaning of the root word?

   a. _____turn   _____

   b. _____form   _____

   c. _____examine   _____

2. Complete the following examples of similes.

   a. as fancy as _____

   b. fluffy like _____

3. Draw a vertical line between the complete subject and the complete predicate.
   Ex: Birds / are the only animals that have feathers.

   a. The ostrich is the largest bird in the world.

   b. Down feathers keep birds warm in cold weather.

   c. Penguins use their wings as flippers to help them swim faster.

   d. Birds build many different types of nests.

   e. Baby birds are always hungry.

4. Read the following sentences. If it is a complete sentence, write **C** in the space provided. If it is a fragment, write **F**.

   a. _____When I travel on the bus.

   b. _____This road has some dangerous curves.

   c. _____Going to the beach this afternoon.

   d. _____Since you will not be able to come with us.

   e. _____The beautiful green forest.

5. Identify each of the following types of sentences. On the line next to each sentence write **D** for declarative, **I** for interrogative, **Imp** for imperative, or **E** for exclamatory, and fill in the correct punctuation at the end of sentence.

a. ....Watch out for that bee

b. ....Why do bees fly from flower to flower

c. ....Bees collect nectar from the flowers

d. ....What hard workers they are

Icicles were forming on Sham's feelers, yet his body was wet with sweat. He backed up. He lowered his head, and as the whip struck him, he made a snatching pull. The load moved, and as if by some supernatural power Sham kept on going up the incline. When almost at the top, however, his forefeet began slipping. He clawed with them. The whip snarled and cracked. It cut deep into his hide. Groaning, he tried again. His veins swelled to bursting.

King of the Wind by Marguerite Henry.
Used by permission, Macmillan Publishing Co.

1. a. Read the literature passage. Copy the passage from dictation and compare your copy to the model. Correct any errors.

b. Look at the fifth sentence of the literature passage and find the prefix **fore-**. This prefix means *before in time*. Does knowing the meaning of this prefix help you to understand the meaning of the word *forefeet*? Add this prefix to your prefix list along with its definition and some word examples.

c. Look over the first sentence of the literature passage. Why is an apostrophe used in *Sham's feelers*? ....

Review the rules for use of apostrophes in Lesson 6 if you are not sure.

d. Choose two to six words for your spelling words or use the following suggested list:

snatching	snarled	cracked
groaning	tried	slipped

....

....

....

e. Note that each of the spelling words has the suffix **-ed** or **-ing**. Usually words with these suffixes are verbs; however, one of these words is used as an adjective. Read each of the words in the context of the sentence in the literature passage. Can you identify the word that is used as an adjective? ....

f. In Lessons 4 and 7, you learned *Spelling Tips* for adding suffixes to words. Two of the tips are as follows:

Drop the silent e from a word before adding a suffix that begins with a vowel.

When a one-syllable word ends with a short vowel followed by a consonant, then the last consonant is doubled before adding a suffix beginning with a vowel.

Find the word in the suggested Spelling List that follows one of these *Spelling Tips* and tell your teacher which rule it follows.

....

....

g. Find the word *tried* in the suggested spelling list. The **y** in the root word *try* has been changed to an **i** before the suffix **-ed** was added.

Spelling Tip
When a word ending in **y** is preceded by a consonant, the **y** is changed to **i** before adding a suffix, except for a suffix beginning with **i** such as **-ing**. If a word ends with **y** preceded by a vowel, then just add the suffix.

Copy these words. Say the words aloud as you write them. Remember there is no change made in the root word when adding the suffix **-ing**.

Root Word

play _____

hurry _____

empty _____

carry _____

-ing

playing _____

hurrying _____

emptying _____

carrying _____

-ed

played _____

hurried _____

emptied _____

carried _____

h. Add the suffixes **-ed** and **-ing** to the following words. Be sure to follow the rules for adding suffixes.

Root Word   **-ed**   **-ing**
Ex: fry   fried   frying
       stay   stayed   staying

1) marry ....

2) cry ....

3) pray ....

4) chop ....

5) sneeze ....

6) stray ....

7) trade ....

8) drip ....

9) apply ....

10) copy ....

a. A sentence expresses a complete thought and has two parts, the complete subject and the complete predicate.
    Ex: Three boys / were playing basketball.
           (complete subject) (complete predicate)

b. The **simple subject** of a sentence is the noun or pronoun that is the focal point of the complete subject without any modifiers (adjectives).
    Ex: Three boys / were playing basketball.
           (*boys* is the simple subject)

c. The **simple predicate** of a sentence is the verb or verb phrase that tells the action of the subject without any modifiers (adverbs). A verb phrase is the main verb and one or more helping verbs.
    Ex: Five girls / played tennis.
           (*played* is the simple predicate or verb)

           Three boys / were playing basketball.
           (*were playing* is the simple predicate or verb phrase)

d. Look at the last sentence of the literature passage. Divide the complete subject and complete predicate with a vertical line. Underline the simple subject and circle the simple predicate.

e. Often sentences contain more than one simple subject. A **compound subject** consists of two or more subjects. Look at the following sentence:

Sara and Anna had a wonderful time at the park.

This sentence has a compound subject since both *Sara* and *Anna* are part of the complete subject.

Sentences with more than one verb (or simple predicate) have a **compound verb**.
Ex: Joe went to the store and bought some milk.

Since both the verbs, *went* and *bought*, are telling what action was taken by the subject, *Joe*, the sentence has a compound verb.

f. Find a sentence in the literature passage that contains a compound verb. Double underline the compound verb.

g. Write one sentence with a compound subject and one with a compound verb.

_____

_____

_____

_____

_____

3. a. A **conjunction** is a connecting word used to connect words, groups of words, or sentences.

Common Conjunctions
and   but   or   nor   so   yet

b. When two complete sentences are joined together by a conjunction, it forms a
    compound sentence.
    Ex: The two girls went on a picnic together, but they had to return before dark.

    The conjunction *but* connects the two complete sentences:
        The two girls went on a picnic together.
        They had to return before dark.

c. Read over the literature passage. Find three compound sentences connected by
    conjunctions, and circle those conjunctions.

d. In compound sentences, a **comma** is always used before the coordinating conjunction.
    Find the commas that appear before the coordinating conjunctions in the three compound
    sentences.

e. Read the compound sentences from the literature passage as two separate sentences
    leaving out the conjunction. Now read them as the author wrote them. Which way do
    you like better?

f. Read the literature passage again. Tell your teacher in your own words what is
    happening. What information is not given? What words give you a clear picture of the
    scene? Write a paragraph to add to the passage, explaining what may have happened
    next. Use words that enable the reader to envision a clear picture of the events. Try to use
    compound sentences.

    ....

    ....

    ....

    ....

    ....

    ....

    ....

g. Practice writing your spelling words. Keep in mind the rules for adding suffixes as you
    practice your words.

Enrichment
Read each list of words. Decide which word is the most general in that category and list it first. Next, list the word that is more specific, and finally the one that is the most specific.

Example: tree
                  oak   --------> plant, tree, oak
                  plant

1. bread
   dough --------->
   flour

2. vehicle
   race car -------->
   car

3. Little League
   sport -------->
   baseball

4. food
   beans -------->
   vegetable

5. shirt
   clothes -------->
   sweatshirt

6. book
   Carry On, Mr. Bowditch -------->
   novel

a. The author of the literature passage makes good use of adjectives, adverbs, and descriptive verbs to create a word picture that helps you to not only see, but feel and hear what was happening. For example, instead of just saying "The whip struck him.", the author describes it as "The whip snarled and cracked." Reread the literature passage and examine the author's use of descriptive language.

b. Today you are going to write a paragraph describing a strenuous activity. You could describe a sport you enjoy, or describe an active animal such as a cat stalking prey.

c. Begin by brainstorming about your ideas. Choose your subject, such as the cat. You will draw a circle word picture. Write your subject in the circle. On the lines extending from the circle, write your ideas. Record anything that comes to mind. You will use some of the ideas but not all of them. Write down any descriptive words you could use in your paragraph.

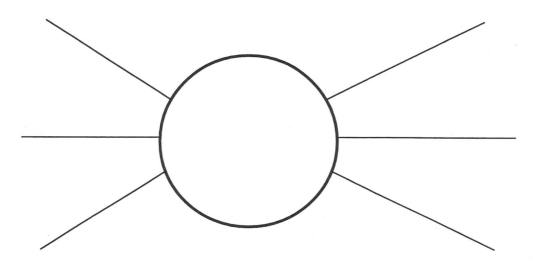

d. Beginning with a good topic sentence, take your ideas and form a good paragraph describing your subject. Create a word picture that will allow anyone who reads your paragraph to imagine he is observing or experiencing the activity.

_____

e. Take an oral or written spelling pretest.

_____

Enrichment
Review the *Enrichment Activity* after Lesson 9, **3g**. Write four lists of words from the general concept to the specific one.
Example: beverage, hot drink, coffee

_____

Illustrate two of your lists.

Choose one of the following activities. Complete on separate paper.

1) Write the literature passage from dictation.

2) Continue to work on your descriptive paragraph from **4a-d**. Draw a picture illustrating the paragraph.

3) Choose skills from the *Review Activities*.

Review Activities

Examine the words listed below that contain the prefix **fore-**. Guess the meaning of each word and then use your dictionary to check the definition. Does knowing the meaning of the prefix **fore-** help you in determining a word's meaning?

a. foredoom ....

b. forefather ....

c. forecast ....

Add the suffixes in parentheses to the following root words.

a. plenty + (ful) = ...

b. buy + (er) = ...

c. hurry + (ing) = ...

d. apply + (ed) = ...

e. busy + (est) = ...

3. Underline the simple subject once and the verb twice in the following sentences.

   a. The tall plant waved in the breeze.

   b. The football player ran down the field for a touchdown.

   c. Mary can knit very quickly.

   d. The garden show will begin in ten minutes.

   e. The white flowers smell very sweet.

4. Underline the conjunctions in the following sentences. On the line before each sentence, write if it contains a compound subject (**CS**), a compound verb (**CV**), or if it is a compound sentence (**CSent**). Also, add punctuation if the sentence is a compound sentence.

   a. _____ The daisies and marigolds made a lovely combination.
   b. _____ The *Nina*, *Pinta*, and *Santa Maria* sailed to America.
   c. _____ We will walk to the park and catch the bus.
   d. _____ I will check with my mother but I do not think I will be able to go to the movie.
   e. _____ The children played games, ate lunch, and listened to a story.
   f. _____ We will go shopping at the mall or we can go to the shopping center.

"At last the hole was cut, and I could push myself in. There was my father right below me, there on the wheel. The wheel was leaning against the side of the boat. With his last strength my father had climbed to the hub to be as close to me as possible while I sawed, to be within reach. I leaned in; I grabbed him under the arms; I lifted him out. I was small, but I was strong. Right then I could have lifted the church and the tower. Too, my father was just a light skeleton."

The Wheel on the School by Meindert DeJong.
Used by permission, Harper and Row.

a. Look over the literature passage taking special notice of the punctuation. What do the quotation marks at the beginning and end of the passage tell you?

Write the literature passage from dictation. Compare your copy to the model and correct any errors.

b. Make a spelling list of any misspelled words from your dictation or use the following suggested list:

skeleton	strength	myself
possible	within	against

Write the spelling words, dividing them into syllables. Remember, each syllable has to contain a vowel.

c. It is important to be familiar with letters that are silent when they appear in certain letter combinations. Some words spell the long /i/ sound with **igh** as in *light*. What letters are silent? _____

> **Spelling Tip**
> Some words spell the long /i/
> sound with **igh** as in **light**.

d. Copy the words and underline the **gh**. Say the words aloud as you write them. Do you ever hear a /g/ sound? _____

1) freight _____   6) bright _____

2) light _____   7) sight _____

3) right _____   8) weight _____

4) might _____   9) might _____

5) height _____   10) twilight _____

e. Sometimes words can be tricky. In the first sentence, the word *hole* is used. How would the meaning change if the author had used the word *whole* instead? The words *hole* and *whole* are homonyms. **Homonyms** are words that sound the same, have different meanings, and are usually spelled differently.

Whole means entire, and *hole* means an opening. When writing, be careful to use the correct word.

f. Listed below are six words from the literature passage that have corresponding homonyms. List the homonyms for each word. Be careful, some words have more than one homonym.
Ex: eight - ate

1) right _____   4) too _____

2) there _____   5) in _____

3) be _____   6) I _____

g. Choose one set of homonyms and write a sentence using all the homonyms for that word in the sentence.
Ex: The *eight* of us *ate* supper at the deli.

_____

_____

a. The person telling a story is called the **narrator**. The **point of view** is the angle from which the story is told. The point of view will depend upon who is telling the story, whether it is told from the point of view of one of the characters in the story or from the point of view of someone outside the story.

b. The **first person** point of view is when the story is told from the point of view of one of the story characters. One indication that a story is being told from the first person point of view is the use of the pronoun *I* in the telling of the story. Although the character is usually a person, the character telling the story could be an animal or even an object.
Ex: *I* was breathless with anticipation as the box was opened.

c. The **third person** point of view is used when the story is told from the point of view of someone outside the story. The use of the pronouns he, she, and they often indicate the use of third person.
Ex: *She* was breathless with anticipation as the box was opened.

d. Examine the literature passage. From what point of view is this story being told?

_____

Does the context of the passage let you know who the narrator is?

_____

Which words give you clues in identifying the narrator?

_____

e. Examine some other stories and determine the point of view from which they are written.

f. Rewrite the literature passage into the third person point of view. Look over the two versions of the literature passage. Which version do you find more enjoyable to read? Why?

_____

_____

_____

_____

_____

_____

_____

_____

_____

_____

_____

_____

a. Locate the three separate sentences joined together by semicolons (;) in the literature passage. The use of semicolons indicates that each part of the sentence is independent and could stand alone. An **independent clause** contains a complete thought which can stand alone as a sentence. **Semicolons** are used to join together independent clauses when they are not connected by a conjunction.

Ex: The wind blew through the trees; the leaves rustled.

Phrases that do not contain both subject and predicate are not independent. They are often listed together in a series with a conjunction joining the last phrase or item of the series. When three or more phrases or items are used together in a series, commas are used to separate the phrases or items, with a final comma used before the conjunction.

Ex: I will be driving to the store, shopping for some groceries, and coming home.
       I love the peaches, plums, and nectarines that are ripe this time of year.

Find the three independent clauses in the literature passage that are joined by semicolons. Rewrite them into one good sentence containing phrases in a series. Some words will have to be omitted, but the meaning of the sentence should not change. Be sure to use commas to separate the phrases.

_____

_____

_____

_____

b. Having only one paragraph from an entire book restricts your information. However, there are certain things revealed in the literature passage. It can be determined there is a struggle taking place. Can you guess what is happening?

_____

_____

_____

c. Reread the literature passage. Can you tell how the person telling the story feels?

_____

_____

The emotion created by the author is called the **mood** of the story. A good author uses descriptions that draw the reader into the action happening in the story and allows the reader to share in the mood created. How would you describe the mood created in this paragraph?

_____

Discuss with your teacher how the author succeeded in creating this mood.

d. How would you feel if you were trying to rescue your father or a friend? Write a paragraph describing a tense situation. Use descriptions that create the mood you want and help the reader to feel what you feel.

_____

_____

_____

_____

_____

_____

_____

_____

_____

_____

e. Review your spelling words and prepare for a practice test.

Enrichment

Read each pair of words and decide how they are connected to each other. Choose one of the categories in the box.

---

synonym such as big : large   **antonym** such as big : small
part/whole such as petal : flower   **category** such as baseball : sport
characteristic such as knife : sharp

---

1) open : closed _____

2) Mars : planet _____

3) fast : quick _____

4) branch : tree _____

5) rock : hard _____

6) moist : dry _____

7) Jim : boy _____

8) bucket : pail _____

9) glass : fragile _____

10) letter : word _____

Illustrate two word pairs.

4. a. Every story has a plot. The **plot** is the sequence of events and actions that take place in the story. Every good plot contains five main elements:

Plot Line

1) **Opening**: This is the part of the story that introduces the characters, explains the background of the story, the setting, and the present situation.

2) **Rising Action**: This is a series of problems and struggles which are building toward a climax.

3) **Climax**: The climax is the turning point or action peak of the story. Usually this is the point at which the action and anticipation is at the fullest.

4) **Falling Action**: The point in the story at which the action of the turning point or high point is worked out and a solution is at hand.

5) **Conclusion**: The part of the story in which the solution comes to a conclusion and the problem is solved. This usually provides the story with its ending.

A graphic representation of the elements of the plot of a story is called a **plot line**. A plot line can help you envision the sequence of the elements and how they are put together to form the plot of a story.

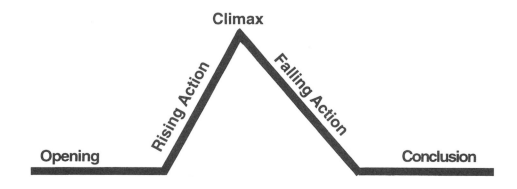

b. Which element of the plot is present in the literature passage?

Which sentence of the passage best describes the turning point or action peak?

c. Although the literature passage only supplies us with a small amount of information concerning the situation, it does allow us to speculate what problems might have occurred prior to the rescue. These problems would be considered part of the rising action of the story. Imagine what problems would lead up to the situation described in the literature passage. Write a paragraph or two describing events and problems that lead up to the climax in the literature passage. Read the paragraphs you have written with the literature passage. Does your version of the rising action supply a series of events that lead up to the climax?

d. Take an oral or written spelling pretest.

Enrichment
Read each pair of words and decide how they are connected to each other. Choose one of the categories in the box.

sequence such as first : second	**degree** such as moist : soaked
homonym such as hi : high	**function** such as stove : cook

1) cool : cold _____

2) knead : need _____

3) knife : cut _____

4) fall : winter _____

5) knight : night _____

6) warm : hot _____

7) book : read _____

8) 34 : 35 _____

Illustrate two word pairs.

5. a. Choose one of the following activities. Complete on separate page.

   1) Write the literature passage from dictation.

   2) Write a short story that contains the five elements of a plot. Map out your ideas on a plot line to make sure you have all the ingredients necessary for a effective plot.

   3) Choose skills from the *Review Activities* on the next page.

Review Activities

1. Underline the correct word in the parentheses to complete the sentence.

a. (*There*, *Their*) will be a children's concert this evening.

b. We will be going (*to*, *too*) the pottery class soon.

c. I will (*right*, *write*) to my friend in Ireland.

d. The (*be*, *bee*) kept buzzing around her head.

e. The (*in*, *inn*) was already full when Mary and Joseph came.

2. Read over the following paragraph.

> I surveyed all the land below me with a careful and calculated eye looking for the slightest possible movement. The rustle of a leaf, a shift of a blade of grass was all that was necessary to lead me to my prey. Suddenly, it happened! I detected movement! Quick as a flash I swooped from my treetop vantage point and clutched a small mouse in my talons.

Who is the narrator? _____

From what point of view is the story is told? _____

What mood has been created? _____

3. Add commas as necessary.

a. On our summer vacation we will visit the seashore climb a mountain and ride a horse.

b. I looked inside reached down and picked up the rabbit.

c. For the party I need to buy balloons cake decorations and gifts.

d. The bumblebee buzzed flipped and dove around the flowers.

e. My grandparents have visited England France and Spain.

f. Bring your lunch a thermos and a blanket.

4. What are the five main elements to a good plot?

> *Everybody laughed, but the teacher's eyes weren't pleased. "True, true," he said. "That's right, Eelka. We can't think much when we don't know much. But we can wonder! From now until tomorrow morning when you come to school again, will you do that? Will you wonder why and wonder why? Will you wonder why storks don't come to Shora to build their nests on the roofs, the way they do in all the villages around? For sometimes when we wonder, we can make things begin to happen."*

The Wheel on the School by Meindert Dejong.
Used by permission, Harper and Row.

1. a. Read the literature passage paying special attention to the punctuation marks. Write the passage from dictation. Proofread and correct your work.

b. The literature passage contains four contractions. Locate the contractions and circle them. List each of the contractions, and write the two words that make up each contraction next to it.

_____

_____

c. Find the word in the literature passage that is using an apostrophe (') to show possession, and underline it. What is it showing possession of? _____

d. Make a spelling list from any misspelled words from your dictation or use the following suggested list:

tomorrow	villages	happen
wonder	around	morning

_____

_____

_____

e. Look through the literature passage and find nouns that are plural (more than one). A noun is made plural by adding **s** or **es** to the word. The nouns in the literature passage have been made plural by adding just **s**.

> ### Spelling Tip
> Most nouns form their plural form by just adding **s**. However, to form the plural of nouns ending in **sh, ch, x, s**, and **z**, add **es**. In words that end in **y** preceded by a consonant, change the **y** to **i** and add **es**. If the word ends in **y** preceded by a vowel, then just add **s**.

Ex: beach - beaches   wish - wishes   box - boxes   glass - glasses
     waltz - waltzes   puppy - puppies   ray - rays

f. Add **s** and **es** to your list of suffixes. Under parts of speech write *forms plural nouns*. These suffixes have no meanings. Be sure to fill in some word examples.

g. Write each of the following nouns in its plural form.

1) cherry _____   6) dress _____

2) dish _____   7) church _____

3) boy _____   8) daisy _____

4) fox _____   9) insect _____

5) rock _____   10) buzz _____

a. As you learned in Lesson 10, every plot has at least one conflict or problem to be resolved. From reading the literature passage, can you identify the main conflict in *The Wheel on the School?*

_____

_____

b. Can you determine the mood of the teacher in the literature passage?

_____

_____

What do you think the teacher was challenging the students to do?

_____

_____

c. Find the direct quotation in the literature passage.

The quotation is divided with the words *he said*. When the quotation is divided after a complete sentence, both parts of the quotation are completely enclosed by quotation marks.

Ex: "I love a rainy spring day," said Mary. "I can't wait until the flowers begin blooming."

If the quotation is divided within a sentence, then the second part of the quotation does not begin with a capital letter. This is called a **split quotation**.

Ex: "I need to finish my chores," answered Mark, "and then I will be able to join you."

d. Along with the rules of punctuation for divided quotations, be sure to follow the following rules when punctuating direct quotations.

1) Enclose only the exact words of the speaker with quotation marks.
2) Capitalize the first word of a direct quotation.
3) Punctuation (commas, periods, question marks, and exclamation points) appears inside the quotation marks when it applies to the direct quote.
4) The exact words of the speaker are separated from the rest of the sentence by a comma, question mark, or exclamation point.
5) When the direct quotation is more than one sentence and is not divided, then quotation marks should be used at the beginning of the quote and the end of the quote. Quotation marks should not enclose each sentence separately.

Add capitalization and punctuation, including quotation marks, commas, question marks, exclamation points, and periods to the following direct quotations. (For further information on punctuating direct quotations, refer to Lesson 7.)

1) I will finish my shopping said Jerri and meet you at the game

2) drive to the house slowly said Mary we don't want to arrive too early

3) when will the leaves begin to change color asked Jimmy

4) Marilyn smiled it is a wonderful feeling to know I have such good friend

5) stop playing and start working yelled Natalie with frustration we need to have the float finished by noon

6) spring is in the air. I see birds beginning to build their nests.   a warm breeze is blowing from the south said Anne with a smile

e. Read the literature passage carefully once again. What do you think possibly happened just before this scene? Use your imagination to write a paragraph describing what could have happened.

_____

_____

_____

_____

_____

_____

_____

a. Sentences can ask a question (interrogative), make a statement (declarative), express strong feeling (exclamatory), or give a command (imperative). Find an example of an interrogative, declarative, and exclamatory sentence in the literature passage. Remember, the type of punctuation a sentence has can help you to identify it.

_____

_____

_____

_____

_____

_____

_____

_____

b. Find the three interrogative sentences in the literature passage again. Change these interrogative sentences into imperative sentences. Remember, the subject in an imperative sentence is often understood. Be sure to change the end punctuation.

    Ex: Will you please close the door? (interrogative)

          Please close the door. (imperative)

c. Look at the third sentence of the literature passage. In this sentence, Eelka is addressed by name. This is called a **direct address**. When a name is used in a direct address, set it off with commas. A pair of commas is used if the name appears within the sentence, but only one comma is necessary if the name appears at the beginning or end of the sentence.

    Ex: Go to the kitchen, Nancy, and find my large platter.

          Jack, please help me lift this box.

          You do not have to come with me, Rick.

d. Punctuate the following sentences that use a direct address. Also, be sure to add the correct end punctuation.

1) Martha go see who is at the door

2) I really liked your part in the play William

3) The secret to success Lydia is to prepare for opportunity

4) Carol are you sure the meeting is today

5) Come here this minute Patrick

e. Review your spelling words and prepare for tomorrow's practice test.

Enrichment

Read each pair of words and decide how they are connected to each other. Choose one of the categories in the box.

synonym	antonym	part/whole	category	characteristic
sequence	degree	homonym	function	

1) grape : fruit _____

2) hard : difficult _____

3) baby : toddler _____

4) reed : read _____

5) help : hinder _____

6) rope : bind _____

7) roof : house _____

8) snow : cold _____

9) jog : run _____

10) knead : need _____

11) sun : heat _____

12) wheel : bicycle _____

13) cat : curious _____

14) football : sport _____

15) gigantic : huge _____

a. Many important discoveries have been made or mysteries solved because someone was curious. Someone wondered, "What if? Why? How?" Think about how our lives have been enriched because someone wondered.

b. Eelka's teacher encouraged her students to think. One way to improve your thinking skills is to develop word analogies. A **word analogy** expresses a relationship between words. An analogy statement has two parts. In the first part of the statement two words are placed together that are in some way related, then in the second part of the analogy two different words are placed together that have a similar relationship.
Ex: eyes:sight :: ears:hearing

This word analogy would read: Eyes are to sight as ears are to hearing.

In the above example the relationship is that as eyes provide the sense of sight; ears provide the sense of hearing. There are many different ways words can be related. Some of the relationships used in word analogies are:

antonyms	good:bad :: happy:sad
synonyms	yell:shout :: soaring:flying
part/whole	fingers:hand :: toes:foot
characteristic	leaves:green :: snow:white
function	scissors:cut :: pencil:write
object/place	car:garage :: furniture:house
family	mother:daughter :: father:son
grammar	noun:adjective :: verb:adverb

What type of relationship is used in our example analogy (eyes:sight :: ears:hearing)?

_____

c. Fill in the second part of the word analogies listed below. First decide what the relationship of the first two words is and then apply that relationship to the second part of the word analogy to fill in the blank.

1) fish:water :: cow: _____

2) ant:insect :: dog: _____

3) candy:sweet :: pickle: _____

4) beach:swimming :: mountain: _____

5) petals:flower :: leaves: _____

d. Take an oral or written spelling pretest.

_____

_____

_____

Enrichment

Read the first pair of words in the lists below. Decide what the relationship is between these words. Then read the next word and decide which word from the Word Box will make the same relationship. Write that word in the blank. These are called analogies.

Word Box				
jar	build	bag	knot	tired
fish	cold	run	dull	winter

1. ant:insect :: flounder: _____

2. natural:man-made :: shiny: _____

3. needle:sharp :: ice cube: _____

4. spring:summer :: autumn: _____

5. bucket:pail :: sack: _____

6. dinosaur:enormous :: runner: _____

7. leg:table :: lid: _____

8. artist:create :: carpenter: _____

9. road:rode :: knot: _____

10. chuckle:laugh :: stroll: _____

Illustrate two of the analogies.

a. Choose one of the following activities. Complete on separate paper.

1) Write the literature passage from dictation. "Listen" for the punctuation as your teacher reads the paragraph.

2) Look at the paragraph below. Correct all errors in capitalization, punctuation, and other writing mechanics. When you are finished, compare to model and correct.

everybody laughed but the teachers eyes werent pleased. true true he said. thats right Eelka. we cant think much when we dont know much. but we can wonder. from now until tomorrow morning when you come to school again, will you do that. will you wonder why and wonder why. will you wonder why storks dont come to shora to build their nests on the roofs the way they do in all the villages around. for sometimes when we wonder, we can make things begin to happen.

3) What are some things that cause you to wonder? Write one thing and spend some time wondering about it. You can do this by thinking about it, talking about it, and/or looking up information about it.

4) Choose skills from the *Review Activities* on the next page.

Review Activities

1. Write the plural form of the following words.

   a. brush _____

   b. guess _____

   c. lily _____

   d. turkey _____

   e. ax _____

2. Add quotation marks and punctuation to the following sentences.

   a. We will begin the canoe trip at this point announced Luke and then paddle downstream to the campgrounds

   b. Who is going to the concert asked Adam I will be leaving in an hour

   c. I do not know the answer to the problem said Anna Can you help me

   d. The soccer equipment is expensive at this store remarked Will

   e. Nicki shouted Catch the ball

3. Add punctuation to the following sentences.

   a. Judy will you please open the door for me?

   b. I located the bird nest Kate in the old oak tree.

   c. Explain the bike safety rules to the club Lewis.

4. Fill in the word that correctly finishes the word analogy.

a. black:white :: tall:_____

b. run:sprint :: walk: _____

c. uncle:nephew :: aunt:_____

d. rabbit:hutch :: bird: _____

e. ruler:measure :: spoon: _____

Assessment 2
(Lessons 7 - 11)

1. Give an example of an interrogative sentence.

   What punctuation would you use?

2. Rewrite the following imperative sentence with the subject (*Sarah*) understood but not stated.

   Sarah, put the dog out.

   ....

3. Write a word with the prefix **re-**.

4. Write a sentence with a compound subject.

5. Write a sentence with a compound verb.

6. Circle the conjunction in each of the following sentences.

   a. He ran down the beach and shouted for joy.

   b. We would like to come but cannot at this time.

   c. Sam or Sue could do the job.

7. Combine the following two sentences to form one sentence with a compound verb.

Bob opened the door. Bob stepped aside for his mother.

8. Copy the following sentence, adding the correct punctuation.

Could you come over today Mary asked We could study together

9. Read "The Wind and the Sun." What is the conflict and climax of the story?

The Wind and the Sun

One day a man strolled contentedly down a village road. The Sun warmed the man gently with its rays as he looked up and smiled. At this, the Wind came and taunted, "You think you are so mighty and great, but I will show you that I am stronger than you."

"Very well," said the Sun.

"Whoever has the ability to take the cloak off the man strolling on the road shall be claimed the victor," said the Wind assuredly.

"Very well," said the Sun again. "You may go first."

The Wind bellowed out the fiercest gust of wind that he could but the man held on to his cloak. The Wind blew more ferociously than before. He blew and blew, but the man clutched his cloak tighter.

Now it was the Sun's turn. As the Wind moved over to the side, the Sun gleamed his bright face in the sky. The man loosened his grip. Sun beamed, radiating his warmth to the man below. Looking upward, the man squinted, removed his cloak, and continued on his way.

How To Conduct

Personal
Research

How to Conduct Personal Research

1. a. In last week's lesson we discussed how our lives had been enriched by someone's curiosity. Many times curiosity naturally leads to research. Think of something that interests you. It could be something you desire to purchase: a pet, a bike, computer, or sports equipment. Perhaps you would even like to know which fast food chain offers the highest quality burger. For the next few days you will explore an enjoyable form of research written in the form of a story. Many times the purpose of research is extensive study of a topic with lots of library work. In your personal research story, however, you may use the library if you choose, but you will use a variety of resources as well.

   b. First you must choose a topic. Imagine you are going to purchase a new bike. Think about possible questions to research. What is the purpose of the research? What information do you need to make a wise purchase? Where would you get the best price? Number and list your ideas.

   _____

   _____

   _____

   _____

   _____

   _____

   _____

   _____

2. a. Decide the best way to gather the necessary information. If, for example, you choose to research the topic of bikes, planning a trip to several local bike shops would be a great starting point. Use the *Yellow Pages* to find bike shops that carry different brands. While visiting the shops, gather brochures and any other information they make available. Do a price comparison between bike shops. Prepare a standard list of questions to ask at each shop. Look at the following questions.

   1) Why do you carry this brand of bikes?
   2) Tell me about the quality of your product.
   3) Do your bikes have warranties?
   4) What are your payment options? Could a purchase be put on layaway?
   5) Do you ever have sales?

Take notes and keep track of the information you gather.

5. Plan to interview several friends who own different brands of bikes. Make a list of questions for them. Use the rest of the week to thoroughly gather the following information.

1) Why did you choose this brand over another?
2) Have you enjoyed your bike?
3) Would you purchase this brand again?
4) Have you had any problems with your bike?

Enrichment
Read the first pair of words in the lists below. Decide what the relationship
is between these words. Then read the next word and decide which word
from the Word Box will make the same relationship. Write that word in the blank.

Word Box
army   hit   finish   relax   forget
green   soak   shape   rainbow   fair

1. mitt:catch :: bat: _____

2. aim:goal :: complete: _____

3. bud:blossom :: rain: _____

4. player:team :: soldier: _____

5. king:rule :: holiday: _____

6. hi:high :: fare: _____

7. concrete:hard :: grass: _____

8. exciting:boring :: remember: _____

9. puppy:dog :: moisten: _____

10. guitar:musical instrument :: triangle: _____

Write five of your own analogies. Illustrate two of them.

_____

_____

How to Conduct Personal Research

a. Use a consumer report to read about different bikes. Check your library for a junior version of a standard consumer report.

b. Compare the prices you found in the bike shops to the prices in discount stores. Use these lines for your notes.

_____

_____

_____

_____

2-3.

a. Check to see if you are satisfied with the information you have gathered. If you are prepared to write your research story, follow the steps listed below in organizing your information. Complete on separate paper.

1) Make sure all your information is related to the topic you are writing about.
2) Make a list of the various ideas about your subject that you wish to write about.
3) Group your ideas into several main ideas and number these grouping as to the order in which you want them to appear in your paper.
4) Write an introductory paragraph for your research paper. This paragraph should explain the purpose of your research and give a brief summary of what your paper will be about.
5) Write your supporting paragraphs. Make sure that all the information presented supports the main topic presented in your introductory paragraph.
6) End your paper with a concluding paragraph that again summarizes your topic and ends with a closing sentence.

b. Spend two days compiling your research story. Since this is a research "story," it may be written informally and may include your own opinions and comments. Putting your story in a folder and adding sketches or pictures from brochures would add to the presentation of your research.

4. a. Examine your research story. Was your research helpful in making a decision about your purchase? Would it be helpful to someone else making a similar choice?

b. Check your paper for any errors in spelling, grammar, capitalization, and punctuation.

5. Look over your research story once more. Make a final, neat copy for your teacher.
    Complete on separate paper.

Enrichment

Read the first pair of words in the lists below. Decide what the relationship is between these words. Then read the next word and choose a word that will make the same relationship. Write the word in the blank. You may want to complete this list in two days.

Illustrate three of the analogies

1. car:automobile :: boat: ....

2. summer:season :: Wisconsin: ....

3. sent:scent :: hare: ....

4. earthquake:destructive :: puppy: ....

5. clear:opaque :: war: ....

6. lung:breathe :: knife: ....

7. brick:wall :: minute: ....

8. animal:creature :: infant: ....

9. high school:college :: morning: ....

10. lead:led :: hole: ....

11. stare:stair :: sea: ....

12. worried:confident :: calm: ....

13. sky:blue :: pillow: ....

14. colors:spectrum :: stars: ....

15. fork:utensil :: typhoid: ....

16. stumble:trip :: fast: ....

17. car:transport :: school: ....

18. past:passed :: tale: ....

19. hair:head :: word: ....

20. sweet:sour :: elderly: ....

Jest 'Fore Christmas
by Eugene Field

Father calls me William, sister calls me Will,
Mother calls me Willie, but the fellers call me Bill!
Mighty glad I ain't a girl—ruther be a boy,
Without them sashes, curls, an' things that's worn by Fauntleroy!
Love to chawnk green apples an' go swimmin' in the lake—
Hate to take the castor-ile they give for belly-ache!
'Most all the time, the whole year round, there ain't no flies on me,
But just 'fore Christmas I'm as good as I kin be!

Got a yeller dog named Sport, sic him on the cat;
First thing she knows she doesn't know where she is at!
Got a clipper sled, an' when us kids goes out to slide,
'Long comes the grocery cart, an' we all hook a ride!
But sometimes when the grocery man is worrited an' cross,
He reaches at us with his whip, an' larrups up his hoss,
An' then I laff an' holler, "Oh, ye never teched me!"
But jest 'fore Christmas I'm as good as I kin be!

Gran'ma says she hopes that when I git to be a man,
I'll be a missionarer like her oldest brother, Dan,
As was et up by the cannibuls that lives in Ceylon's Isle,
Where every prospeck pleases, an' only man is vile!
But Gran'ma she has never been to see a Wild West show,
Nor read the Life of Daniel Boone, or else I guess she'd know
That Buff'lo Bill an' cowboys is good enough for me!
Excep' jest 'fore Christmas, when I'm good as I kin be!

And then old Sport he hangs around, so solemn-like an' still,
His eyes they keep a-saying': "What's the matter, little Bill?"
The old cat sneaks down off her perch an' wonders what's become
Of them two enemies of hern that used to make things hum!
But I am so perlite an' 'tend so earnestly to biz,
That Mother says to Father: "How improved our Willie is!"
But Father, havin' been a boy hisself, suspicions me
When, jest 'fore Christmas, I'm as good as I kin be!

For Christmas, with its lots an' lots of candies, cakes, an' toys,
Was made, they say, for proper kids, an' not for naughty boys;
So wash yer face an' bresh yer hair, an' mind yer p's and q's,
An' don't bust out yer pantaloons, and don't wear out yer shoes;
Say "Yessum" to the ladies, an' "Yessur" to the men,
An' when they's company, don't pass yer plate for pie again;
But, thinkin' of the things yer'd like to see upon that tree,
Jest 'fore Christmas be as good as yer kin be!

1. a. Listen as your teacher reads the bolded section of the poem. Does the pronunciation of the words used in the poem sound different than the way you speak? Sometimes an author will use pronunciation peculiar to a certain region, called **dialect**, to express himself. This is an effective way to make his character seem true to life. What are some examples of regional dialect in the first stanza of this poem? Try reading the first two stanzas of the poem aloud.

   _____

   _____

   _____

   b. Look over the poem. Note that the first word of every line of the poem is capitalized. Often in poetry the first word of every line is capitalized even when the word does not begin a sentence.

   c. Find the phrase in the poem that is repeated in each stanza.

   _____

   The technique of repeating a phrase or word in a poem for emphasis or for rhythm is called **repetition**. What effect does the use of repetition have in this poem?

   _____

   _____

   d. Look over your list of dialect words and pronounce them the way they are spelled. Sometimes words are purposely misspelled to allow for dialect pronunciation.

Listed below are some of the words in the literature passage which are misspelled for this purpose. Find the words in the literature passage, and use context clues to decide what the correct word for the dialect word would be. Opposite each of the words write the proper spelling.

Ex: ruther - rather

1) 'fore ....

2) kin ....

3) an' ....

4) laff ....

5) perlite ....

6) prospeck ....

7) hisself ....

8) jest ....

9) thinkin' ....

10) worrited ....

11) castor-ile ....

a. Read the entire poem today.

b. Rewrite the first two stanzas in standard English.

Read each version aloud. Which do you like better? ....

Can you see how effective the use of dialect can be? _____

c. Look over the poem again. Circle any words that are capitalized other than at the
beginning of a line poetry and the pronoun *I*. In Lesson 6 you learned that words were
capitalized for three main reasons:
1) to indicate the beginning of a sentence
2) to help the reader quickly identify proper names and titles
3) to show respect when referring to God and the Bible
Which of the reasons listed is the reason for the capitalization of the words you circled?
Note that Christmas, the name of a holiday, is considered a proper name. The names of
holidays are always capitalized.

_____

_____

_____

_____

_____

_____

d. Find the capitalized words that also indicate a family relationship. When a family
relationship word is used in place of a name or in front of a person's name, the word is
capitalized. However, when the word is not used to replace a name or is used with a
personal pronoun such as my, our, or her, then the word is not capitalized.
Ex: Grandpa Joe came for a visit.
        Grandpa came for a visit.
        My grandpa came for a visit.

e. Correct any errors in capitalization in the following sentences as needed.

1) My Mother said I could go when I am finished.

2) Where is your Father going?

3) Aunt mary and uncle ralph will be visiting this week.

4) When will Grandma be arriving?

5) It will be wonderful to have all the Aunts and Uncles visit for christmas.

a. Poetry that rhymes usually follows a certain pattern called a **rhyme scheme**. In order to identify the rhyme scheme, assign a letter to each line that rhymes. For example, the rhyme scheme for the first stanza of "Jest 'Fore Christmas" is **aabbccdd**, because the last word in the first two lines rhyme (**aa**), the last word in the next two lines is a new rhyme (**bb**), and so on. Does the second stanza follow the same rhyme scheme?

b. Read the following poetry selections by Robert Louis Stevenson. Assign a letter to each line that rhymes and identify the rhyme schemes of the stanzas of the poems.

(*from*) **Where The Boats Go**

> *Dark brown is the river,*
> *Golden is the sand.*
> *It flows along forever,*
> *With trees on either hand.*

(*from*) **Autumn Fires**

> *Sing a song of seasons!*
> *Something bright in all!*
> *Flowers in the summer,*
> *Fires in the fall!*

c. The poems you have been reading have only end rhyme. Other poems rhyme words within a line of poetry to create **internal rhyme.**
    Ex: Jack *Sprat* could eat no *fat*.

Note that the words *Sprat* and *fat* rhyme within the same line of the poem creating an internal rhyme.

d. Read the selections below, find the internal rhymes, and underline them. Remember, in order for a poem to have internal rhyme the words that rhyme must be within one line of the poem.

Whisky Frisky

author unknown

Whisky Frisky,
Hippity-hop
Up he goes
To the treetop!

Whirly, twirly,
Round and round,
Down he scampers
To the ground.

Intery, Mintery, Cutery Corn

Mother Goose Rhyme

Intery, mintery, cutery corn,
Apple seed and apple thorn
Wire, brier, limber-lock,
Three geese in a flock;
One flew east, and one flew west,
And one flew over the cockoo's nest.

e. Write the end rhyme schemes for "Whisky Frisky" and "Intery, Mintery, Cutery Corn." Do you like the effect created when the poet combines end rhyme and internal rhyme?

_____

_____

a. Another device used in poetry is the repetition of beginning consonant sounds within a poem. This is called **alliteration**.
   Ex: **D**iddle, **d**iddle, **d**umpling, my son John,

The consonant **d** is repeated in this example of alliteration. When alliteration is used often throughout the poem, it has a tongue-twisting effect. Read the following example:

Peter Piper
Mother Goose Rhyme

Peter Piper picked a peck of pickled peppers;
A peck of pickled peppers Peter Piper picked.
If Peter Piper picked a peck of pickled peppers,
Where's the peck of pickled peppers Peter Piper picked?

b. "Jest 'Fore Christmas" is about a rather naughty boy. Can you imagine him with a very good little sister? Using this poem as a model, write another poem from the sister's point of view.

Ex: *Father calls me Millicent, brother calls me Mills,*
      Mother calls me Milly, and dresses me in frills!
      Mighty glad I'm not a boy, glad to be a girl,
      Wouldn't touch a frog or toad for anything in the world!
      Love to dress up pretty and have tea parties in the lane,
      Hate to be a bother, or cause anyone the slightest pain.

_____

_____

_____

_____

_____

c. Using the example poem in **4b**, complete the last two lines. Remember to follow the rhyme scheme and to use Mr. Field's poem as your model. After you have completed your poem read the original version and the poem from the sister's point of view. Which version do you like better?

_____

d. The literature passage poem is fun to memorize and recite. Try to memorize just the first stanza of the poem. Follow these tips when reciting poetry or any oral presentation.

Tips on Poetry Recitation

1) Read the poem aloud several times. Try to understand the meaning and the mood of the poem.

2) Use your voice where emphasis is needed and pause accordingly.

3) Speak clearly and loudly.

4) Look at your audience as if you are speaking directly to them.

5) Stand straight; do not slouch.

---

5. a. Choose one of the following activities. Complete on separate paper.

   1) Continue rewriting the other stanzas of the poem from the sister's point of view.

   2) Examine a book of poetry. Try to find examples of poems with internal rhyme and alliteration. Write the rhyme scheme for some of the poems with end rhyme.

   3) Decide what rhyme scheme you like best and write an original poem that uses that rhyme scheme.

   4) Choose skills from the *Review Activities* on the next page.

Review Activities

1. Read the following poem. What is the rhyme scheme? ....
   Identify the following elements:

   alliteration ....

   internal rhyme ....

   end rhyme ....

   repetition ....

> *Roaring, rippling river races toward the sea.*
> *Swirling, twirling waters laugh with joyful glee.*
> *Listen to the waters, listen to them sing.*
>
> *Whipping, whirling waves crashing on the shore.*
> *Reeling, keeling ocean groans and moans its lore.*
> *Listen to the waters, listen to them sing.*

2. Capitalize the names of the following holidays.

   a. independence day ....

   b. fourth of july ....

   c. memorial day ....

   d. thanksgiving day ....

3. Identify the words and expressions in the following paragraph that indicate a regional dialect.

   She ain't a purty horse, like sum are, but she shure is a strong one. Then again, them brown eyes of hers have a way of lookin' at ya that let ya know she's a smart one too.

   ....

   ....

   ....

The pigeons now flew up to crevices in the rocks, the fowls perched themselves on our tent pole, and the ducks and geese waddled off cackling and quacking, to the marshy margin of the river. We, too, were ready for repose, and having loaded our guns and offered up our prayers to God, thanking Him for His many mercies to us, we commended ourselves to His protecting care, and as the last ray of light departed, closed our tent and lay down to rest.

The Swiss Family Robinson by Johann Wyss.

1. a. Read the literature passage. Write the passage from dictation. Proofread your copy. Make any necessary corrections.

b. In the last sentence of the literature passage the family thanks God "for his many mercies." What mercies do you think this family was thankful for?

Are there mercies in your life for which you are thankful?

_____

_____

c. Find the word in the last sentence of the literature passage that contains the prefix **re-**.
Check with your prefix list and find the meaning of **re-**. Often knowing the meaning of a
prefix can help you define an unfamiliar word. The root of *repose* is *pose*. *Pose* means *to
be in a certain position*. The prefix **re-** means *back* or *again*. When you put the prefix
and root together, you have *back position* as a possible choice to help you define the
word *repose*. *Repose* means *to lay at rest*, therefore, *back position* gives a good hint as to
the definition of the word.

d. Find the prefixes **pro-** and **de-** in the last sentence of the literature passage. The prefix **de-**
means *from* or *down* and the prefix **pro-** means *forward* or *in favor of*. Add these
prefixes to your prefix list along with their definitions and words examples. Combine the
meaning of the prefix with the root of the some of the word examples.

Does it help you to define the word? _____

e. Use any words you misspelled in your dictation for your spelling words or use the
following suggested list:

ourselves	crevices	themselves
margin	repose	offered

_____

_____

_____

f. The words ourselves and themselves contain the plural of the words self, spelled **s-e-l-v-e-
s**. The **f** is changed to **v** before the **es** is added because the **/f/** sound in self changes to a
/v/ sound in selves.

In order to determine if the **f** or **fe** should be changed to **v** in order to form a plural, say
the plural of the noun. If you hear a **/v/** sound, then make the change; if you do not hear
a **/v/** sound, then just add **s**.

Ex: reef - reefs

Spelling Tip
When forming the plural of a word ending in **f** or **fe**, change the f or **fe** to **v** and add **es**. If the /f/ sound remains, just add **s**.

g. Write the plural form of the following nouns.

1) wife _____   5) self _____

2) leaf _____   6) roof _____

3) life _____   7) chief _____

4) calf _____   8) wolf _____

2. a. Look over the literature passage and list ten pronouns. Remember, pronouns are words that take place of nouns. Refer to the Personal Pronoun Chart in Lesson 4 if you need help.

_____

_____

_____

_____

_____

b. Personal pronouns may also be classified into persons; either first, second, or third persons.

Personal Pronouns			
First Person (The one speaking)	I we	my, mine our, ours	me us
Second Person (The one being spoken to)	you	you, yours	
Third Person (The one being spoken about)	he she it they	his her, hers its their, theirs	him her them

A **first person pronoun** is the one speaking.
Ex: I took the bus to town.
        I is used as a first person pronoun.

A **second person pronoun** is the one being spoken to.
Ex: You come with me immediately!
        You is used as a second person pronoun.

A **third person pronoun** is the one being spoken about.
Ex: Frequently, Bill visits his grandmother.
        His is used as a third person pronoun. Bill is not the person speaking or being
        spoken to, but he is being spoken about.

c. Once again look at your list of personal pronouns from the literature passage. Indicate if
    they are first, second, or third person pronouns by writing 1, 2, or 3 by them.

d. You learned in Lesson 10 that a story is told from a first person point of view or third
    person point of view. Read over the literature passage and decide from what point of
    view this story is being told. The pronouns used can help you to identify the correct
    point of view.

Enrichment
Word Search Puzzle
Find the plural words for *wife*, *leaf*, *life*, *calf*, *self*, *roof*, and *chief*.

```
n e l r o o f s o x r
c w r o c a l v e s t
c i j u b s e p g e b
t v a n s l a t e l g
j e r t l i v e s v e
p s i r a r e a a e e
c h i e f s s o i s v
```

3. a. Look at the literature passage and underline all the plural nouns. Note that most plurals
       are formed by adding **s** or **es**. However, some nouns form plurals by changing the
       spelling of the word.
       Ex: man - men

    Locate the word in your list of plural nouns that follows this rule. _____

b. Circle the plural that requires the **y** ending to be changed before the **s** is added.

c. Look over the following summary of the spelling rules for forming plurals you have
    covered so far.

> **Spelling Tips for Plurals**
> 1) To form the plural of most words just add **s**.
> 2) To form the plural of nouns ending in **ch, s, sh, x,** or **z** add **es**.
> 3) To form the plural of a noun ending in **y** preceded by a consonant, change the **y** to **i** and add **es**.
> 4) To form the plural of most words ending in **f** or **fe**, change the **f** to **v** and add **es**. If the plural word keeps the **/f/** sound, just add **s**.
> 5) Some words change their spelling to form the plural form.

d. Using these *Spelling Tips*, write the correct plural form for the following nouns.

1) shelf _____   6) woman _____

2) monkey _____   7) loaf _____

3) church _____   8) mass _____

4) box _____   9) baby _____

5) sock _____   10) company _____

e. Review your spelling words for a practice test tomorrow.

4. a. A capital letter is always used when referring to God or the Bible, even if it is a pronoun. Find the three pronouns in the literature passage that are used in reference to God and underline them.

b. Many words are tricky and good writers must exercise extra care not to misuse them. Find the word *lay* used in the last sentence of the literature passage. Locate this example and circle it. The word *lay* is often confused with the word *lie*. If you know the meaning of each word, it will help you to use the correct word when writing.

lay - to put or place something down
     lay, laying, laid, (have) laid
     Please *lay* the paper on my desk.

lie - to rest or recline
     lie, lying, lay, (have) lain
     It is time for you to *lie* down and go to sleep.

Although both words are verbs, only the word *lay* has an object. Look at this sentence again.

    Please *lay* the paper on my desk.

The object is paper. The word *lay* usually has an object, but the word *lie* never has an object.

c. Some other troublesome words are *to*, *too*, *two*. These words are homonyms, words with the same sound but different meanings. Again, being familiar with the meaning of each word will help you choose the correct word.

to - to move toward or in the direction of
    We will be going to the park this afternoon.

too - also
    He is on the team, too.

two - a number
    I need to buy two apples.

d. Choose the correct word.

    1) My cat likes to (*lay*, *lie*) in front of the fireplace.

    2) Make sure you (*lay*, *lie*) your clothes out for the next day.

    3) Do you want to see the movie (*to*, *too*)?

    4) What friend do you want (*too*, *to*) visit?

    5) (*Lay*, *Lie*) down and rest before the trip home.

    6) Do the (*two*, *too*) of you want to come along for the ride?

    7) (*Lay*, *Lie*) your books on the table.

    8) Your game has been (*laying*, *lying*) on the floor all day.

    9) The tiger was (*laying*, *lying*) in wait for its prey.

    10) I have an appointment for (*two*, *to*) o'clock, (*too*, *to*).

e. Take an oral or written spelling pretest.

Enrichment
Read each phrase below and fill in the blank with an appropriate noun.

the _____ giggles

the _____ shudders

the _____ instructs

the _____ melts

the _____ hardens

the _____ howls

the _____ opens

the _____ entertains

Illustrate two of the phrases above.

5. a. Choose one of the following activities. Complete on separate page.

   1) Write the literature passage from dictation.

   2) Imagine what it would be like to be shipwrecked with your family on an isolated, uninhabited island. Write a few paragraphs telling how you would feel and how you would prepare for living there.

   3) Choose skills from the *Review Activities* on the next page.

Review Activities

Add the prefixes **re-**, **de-**, or **pro-** to each of the following roots. If you are unsure of the meaning of the new word, look it up in the dictionary.

a. _____juvenate (prefix meaning *back* or *again*)
b. _____jector (prefix meaning *forward* or *in favor of*)
c. _____preciate (prefix meaning *from* or *down*)

Rewrite the following paragraph by substituting personal pronouns for the underlined words. Write 1 (*first person*), 2 (*second person*), or 3 (*third person*) above each pronoun to indicate which person the pronoun is. Also, tell from what point of view this story is being told. _____

Marcy loved visiting <u>Marcy's</u> cousin, Jeanette, at <u>Jeanette's</u> farm. <u>Marcy and Jeanette</u> would wake up early in the morning because Jeanette needed to feed all <u>Jeanette's</u> animals. <u>Jeanette</u> had chickens, goats, pigs, and cows. However, Marcy's favorite animals were the horses. Jeannette had two horses named Thunder and Whisper. As soon as the chores were done, <u>Marcy and Jeanette</u> would ride for hours through the woods and pastures. <u>Marcy and Jeanette</u> had such fun together!

3. Circle the correct plural form in each of the following sentences.

   a. Many people dressed as (*elfs*, *elves*) at the party.

   b. We drove through many (*valleys*, *valleies*) on our trip.

   c. The meadow was full of (*daisys*, *daisies*).

   d. All the (*dishs*, *dishes*) must be washed before you can leave.

   e. We must finish putting the garden (*tools*, *tooles*) away before it starts raining.

4. Use each word correctly in a sentence: lie, lay.

   _____

   _____

   _____

   _____

5. Underline the correct word.

   a. We will travel (*to*, *too*) Switzerland on the train.

   b. Will Henry be coming along (*to*, *too*)?

   c. The trip will cost (*too*, *two*) hundred dollars.

6. Capitalize all references to God in the following sentence.

   We worship a holy god, and therefore it is important that we worship him with
   a spirit of reverence and remember that he is a loving, but just god.

Suddenly a mottled green fish, a yard long, with a dark back and white underneath, came to the top. It lifted an enormous head right out of the water, and opened a great white mouth, and shook itself. A little perch flew high in the air. Roger's rod straightened. For a moment the great fish lay close to the top of the water, looking wickedly at the crew of the <u>Swallow</u> *as they looked at it. Then, with a twist of its tail that made a great twirling splash in the water, it was gone.*

Swallows and Amazons by Arthur Ransome.
Used by permission, David R. Godine Publishers Inc.

a. Listen as your teacher reads the literature passage. Write the passage from dictation. Circle every word you are not sure is spelled correctly. Compare your copy with the passage.

b. Make a spelling list from the words you misspelled or use the following suggested list:

     mottled   underneath   enormous
     straightened   twist   swirling

c. Try to imagine the scene described in the literature passage. Describe to your teacher how you think the crew felt when the big one got away. If you'd like, draw a picture of what you think the fish looked like.

d. Find the word *underneath* in the literature passage. This word contains the prefix **under-** which means *beneath*. Although **under** is also a word which can stand alone, in this word it is acting as a prefix. Add the prefix **under-** to your list of prefixes and include the definition and some word examples.

e. Locate all forms of the pronoun *it* in the literature passage and draw a box around them. Remember, an antecedent is the noun that the pronoun stands for. What is the antecedent of *it* in the literature passage?

What is the antecedent for the pronoun *they* in the literature passage?

f. Note that the pronoun *its* used in the last sentence of the literature passage is a possessive pronoun. What is the pronoun showing possession of in this sentence? _____

It is important not to confuse the possessive pronoun *its* with the contraction *it's*. If you are using the pronoun in a sentence, it should be showing possession and should not have an apostrophe. If you are using the contraction, the word should have an apostrophe. You can check to make sure you are using the correct form by substituting the words, *it is*, in the sentence. If the words, *it is*, make sense in the sentence, then the contraction form is correct.

g. Complete the sentences correctly with *its* or *it's*.

a. _____ going to be a beautiful morning.

b. I need to get the horse _____ bridle.

c. The peacock spread _____ tail in a breathtaking display.

d. When the alarm rings, _____ six o'clock.

e. The cat will let you pet _____ kittens.

a. Look at the literature passage. Find and underline the adjectives (words that describe nouns) and circle the nouns they describe.

Ex: <u>mottled, green</u> (fish)

b. Read the paragraph aloud, leaving out the adjectives you underlined. Read it again with the adjectives. What difference do adjectives make?

_____

Which way does the paragraph sound better?

_____

Adjectives help you to picture the scene. Without adjectives it would be hard for you to envision what the author wants you to see. The paragraph would be dull and boring to read without adjectives.

c. Find the two words in the literature passage that end in the suffix **-ly**. These two words are adverbs, words that describe verbs. Look at the sentences where these words are located. Identify the verbs they are describing.

Enrichment
Read each word. Then copy the letters below the capitalized word, changing the letter in the box to make a new word.

1)   H   O   T   Dog

peach

☐ ter

prick

cake

2)   Hot D   O   G

an archaeological

sty

pumpkin

down

3. a. Locate the word *perch* in the literature passage. Although it identifies a kind of fish, it is not capitalized. It is only when a particular variety of fish is identified that the name is capitalized, such as Yellow Perch.
   Ex: pine tree (not capitalized)
          Norfolk Pine (specific name - capitalized)

b. Read the following capitalization rules.

Capitalization Rules

1) Capitalize the name of a club, organization, association, team, or political party.
   Ex: Boy Scouts, Red Cross, Striker Soccer Team, Republican Party

2) Capitalize the names of languages, religions, races, and nationalities.
   Ex: French, Catholic, Indian, African

3) Specific school courses are capitalized, but a field of study is not.
   Ex: History 101 (specific course); history (field of study)

4) The brand name of a product is capitalized, but the common noun that appears after
   the brand name is not capitalized.
   Ex: Whirlpool oven

5) Capitalized the first and all important words in the titles and chapters of books, poems,
   plays, magazines, television programs, art works, movies, newspapers, musical
   compositions, articles and stories.
   Ex: *The Last of the Mohicans* (book); *My Fair Lady* (movie); *New York Times* (newspaper)

6) Capitalize the names of historical events and time periods.
   Ex: French Revolution (event); Middle Ages (time period)

7) Names of people, buildings, pets, boats, planes, trains, planets, bridges, monuments,
   and documents are capitalized.
   Ex: Statue of Liberty (monument); Jupiter (planet); *Titanic* (boat)

8) Capitalize the names of days of the week, months, holidays, and special events, but do
   not capitalize the names of seasons (spring, summer, fall, winter) unless they are part of
   the name of an event.
   Ex: Thursday (day of the week); September (month); Valentine's Day (holiday)
          Spring Livestock Show (event); spring rain storm (season)

9) Capitalize geographical places:
   bodies of water - Lake Superior   mountains - Mount St. Helen
   cities - Birmingham   parks - Yellowstone National Park
   countries - Switzerland   provinces - Alberta
   counties - Pinellas County   sections of the country - the West (do not
   continents - Asia   capitalize when referring to direction
   islands - Hawaiian Islands   only - west of town)
   states - Florida   streets, avenues, etc. - Grand Boulevard,
                                               Twenty- first Street (**Note:** The second
                                               part of the number is not capitalized.)

c. Review the literature passage and find proper nouns that are capitalized. Why are they capitalized?

d. Refer to the capitalization rules to help you choose the correct phrases.

A	B
Ex: __B__ the asian culture	the Asian culture
1) _____ a geometry assignment	a Geometry assignment
2) _____ Fifty-second Street	fifty-second street
3) _____ saturn's orbit	Saturn's orbit
4) _____ lake area 4-H club	Lake Area 4-H Club
5) _____ ocala national forest	Ocala National Forest
6) _____ boy scouts	Boy Scouts
7) _____ Statue of Liberty	Statue of liberty
8) _____ Sony stereo	Sony Stereo
9) _____ the sound of music	The Sound of Music
10) _____ Lake Superior	lake superior

e. Review your spelling words for a practice test tomorrow.

4. a. Adjectives are words that describe nouns. Look at the following sentence:

> *An elephant picked up the peanut with a spoon.*

Look at the words that come before *elephant, peanut,* and *spoon. An, a,* and *the* are special adjectives called **articles**. Articles can be signals to tell you that a noun will follow. Usually, the nouns directly follow the articles. Sometimes other adjectives separate the article from the noun, but a noun always follows an article.
Ex: the round orange

The word *round* separates the article from the noun but the noun, *orange* still follows the article, *the*. Find all the articles in the literature passage and underline them once. Locate the nouns they describe and underline them twice.

b. **Synonyms** are words that have the same or similar meanings. A **thesaurus** is a book of synonyms. Use your thesaurus to find synonyms for the adjectives you underlined in **2a**. Check to make sure your synonym makes sense in the content of the literature passage. For example, the word *great* appears three times as an adjective in the literature passage, but each time its meaning is a little different.

c. Rewrite the literature passage using the synonyms you found. Which way do you like better?

d. Take an oral or written spelling pretest.

Enrichment

Read each word. Then copy the letters below the capitalized word, changing the letter in the box to make a new word.

1) C   A   T   Nap

___ ___ [ ]   chase

chin up [ ] ___ ___

baseball ___ ___ [ ]

___ [ ] ___   and bridle

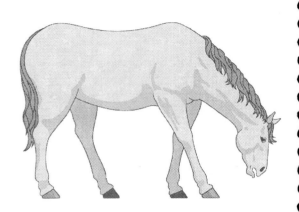

2) Cat   N   A   P

cat ___ [ ] ___

[ ] ___ ___   over

___ ___ [ ]   cup

sun ___ [ ] ___

5. a. Choose one of the following activities. Complete on separate paper.

1) Write the literature passage from dictation again. Did you spell all the words correctly

2) Read the literature passage again. Imagine you are Roger, and you have just battled with a great fish. Its tail makes a splash, and it's gone. How do you feel? Write down your thoughts on paper. Using these ideas, record a journal entry for Roger. A journal entry is written in the first person. This means you are the one speaking or telling the story. Use descriptive words to express how you feel. Edit your work. Check for errors in spelling, punctuation, and writing mechanics.

3) Circle any letters in the following sentences that should be capitalized. If a word is incorrectly capitalized, draw a slash through the letter.

Ex: Many Indians were moved to Reservations as people moved West.

a) Christopher columbus crossed the atlantic ocean to discover america.

b) Her High School schedule included geometry, biology, and word processing 102.

c) Their trip to New York city included visits to the statue of liberty and the empire state building.

d) She is considered bilingual because she can speak both english and spanish fluently.

e) He wasn't sure whether to purchase the Oldsmobile Station Wagon or the Ford Van.

f) There will be no classes on presidents' day and memorial day.

g) The Boy scouts of America will sponsor a food drive at the Glenville baptist church.

h) The directions tell us to turn left at the next Street and follow Bayview avenue to the auditorium.

i) I will be working on tuesday, thursday, and saturday of this Week.

j) We have short Winters and long Summers in the south.

Review Activities

1. Add the prefix **under-** to the following root words. How does the addition of the prefix change the meaning of each word? .... If you are unsure of the meaning of the new word, look it up in the dictionary.

   a. ....line

   b. ....growth

   c. ....age

2. Complete the following paragraph by choosing the correct word.

   The sun is at the center of our solar system. (*Its*, *It's*) gravitational force holds the planets in their orbits. (*Its*, *It's*) known that the sun is made of the gases of hydrogen and helium, and that (*its*, *it's*) surface temperature is about sixty times hotter than boiling water. The sun provides our planet with warmth and light, and (*its*, *it's*) impossible for life to exist without it.

3. Underline any articles you find in the following sentences and draw an arrow to the noun that follows it. Circle any adjectives.

   a. A beautiful border of flowers ran along the garden path.

   b. The array of flowers made the garden a pleasant place to visit.

   c. The visitors enjoyed the colorful butterflies that were attracted by the honeysuckle.

   d. The tiny honeybees buzzed amongst the fragrant blossoms.

   e. An afternoon spent in the lovely garden left you with a peaceful feeling.

4. Underline the adverbs in the following sentence. Circle the verb or verb phrase they modify.

   a. She walked quickly down the sidewalk.

   b. The ground quaked violently beneath their feet.

   c. We seldom travel this road.

   d. She rushed into the room.

   e. We will find the answer tomorrow.

Correct any errors in capitalization by placing a slash through any incorrect letters and placing the correct letter above it.

The Gainesville sun featured an article on the micanopy historical committee's plan to renovate many buildings of historical value in Micanopy. The first methodist church located on twenty-second street will be the first project the committee will undertake. Also many houses built during the civil war are slated to be renovated. The renovations should begin this Spring.

Underline each personal pronoun in the following sentences. Circle the noun that is its antecedent.

a. The mare whinnied at its young foal.

b. The youth group enjoyed their trip to mountains.

c. Jean and Sue went swimming, and then they played volleyball on the beach.

d. Mike usually played first base, but sometimes he played shortstop.

Using a thesaurus, write a synonym for each of the adjectives you circled in the above sentences.

a. beautiful ....

b. tremendous ....

c. rigid ....

d. brittle ....

The

Research Essay

Library Learning

1. Public libraries will be very helpful as you learn to write and research. The librarian has been trained to assist you. If you can't find what you are looking for, ask for help. Most libraries are divided into sections or departments.

   a. **Reference Department** - This is where you will find periodicals, pamphlets/fliers, newspapers, magazines, city/county directories, literary criticisms, consumer reports, and encyclopedias.

   b. **Adult Department** - adult literature, fiction/nonfiction, videos, books on audio tapes, large print books, science fiction, CDs, cassettes.

   c. **Youth Department** - This is where you will find many of your resources. This department is almost like a library in itself containing much of what you find in the reference and adult departments. The books, however, are written for youth. You will find readers of all levels, nonfiction, books on audio tapes, cassettes, encyclopedias, biographies, and a youth reference section.

   d. **Card Catalog** - Here you will find titles, authors, and their reference (call) numbers. In many libraries the card catalog is now obsolete and everything can be found on the library computer.

   Plan a trip to your local library. Ask your librarian to help you become familiar with each department. Ask her to instruct you in using the card catalog or computer.

2. a. There are many books in each department. It would be an overwhelming task to search for a title without the help of the Dewey Decimal System. This system of numbers serves as a way to classify nonfiction books into ten major categories.

Dewey Decimal System

000-099 General Works - encyclopedias, computer information

100-199 Philosophy - conduct, manners

200-299 Religion - Bibles, Bible stories, books about religion, religions of different countries

300-399 Social Science - Folk lore, fairy tales

400-499 Language - dictionaries, sign language, foreign language dictionaries, language helps

500-599 Science - experiments, animals, biology, chemistry, etc.

600-699 Technology - (how things work) health, body, medicine, etc.

700-799 Arts - fine arts, artists, crafts, sports, music, photography

800-899 Literature - (nonfiction) poetry, writing, books, plays

900-999 History/Geography - countries, states, Indians, U.S./World History

---

b. Using the Dewey Decimal System, write the correct number category where you would find the following books.

1) *Earth Science for Every Kid*, Janice Van Cleave _____

2) *The Teenage Book of Manners...PLEASE*, Fred Hartley _____

3) *Intimate Moments with the Savior*, Ken Gire _____

4) *The Thorndike Barnhart Children's Dictionary*, HarperCollins _____

5) *A Child's Treasury of Verse*, Eleanor Doan _____

6) *The Reader's Digest Children's World Atlas* _____

7) *Happy Hours in Storyland* _____

8) *World War II Day by Day*, Donald Sommerville _____

c. During a trip to your library use the Dewey Decimal System to find an example from each category.

_____

_____

_____

_____

_____

_____

_____

_____

Enrichment

Which section in the library is your favorite? _____

Why? _____

Find three books from that section and list the book's name, author, and card catalog number.

_____

_____

_____

3. a. Fiction books (novels, mysteries, etc.) can usually be found in a special section of the library. They are arranged in alphabetical order by the author's last name. If the author has more than one title on the shelf, they are placed in alphabetical order by title.

   Ex: *Summer of the Monkeys*; Rawls, Wilson
        Where the Red Fern Grows; Rawls, Wilson

If the title begins with a small word like *A* or *The*, disregard it, and alphabetize according to the next word. For example, to look up the book title, *The Courage of Sarah Noble*, look under **C** for *Courage*.

b. Arrange the following fiction titles in the order you would find them on the library shelf by placing the order number in the space provided.

.... *Call It Courage*; Sperry, Armstrong

.... *The Tale of Jeremy Vole*; Lawhead, Stephen

.... *Mr. Popper's Penguins*; Atwater, Richard and Florence

.... *The Big Wave*; Buck, Pearl S.

.... *The Tale of Anabelle Hedgehog*; Lawhead, Stephen

.... *Island of the Blue Dolphins*; O'Dell, Scott

.... *Rabbit Hill*; Lawson; Robert

.... *The Sign of the Beaver*; Speare, Elizabeth George

.... *The Road to Damietta*; O'Dell, Scott

.... *Farmer Boy*; Wilder, Laura Ingalls

c. Usually a library has a special section given to biographies and autobiographies. Do you know the difference between the two? If not, use a dictionary to look up the terms. You will find the books in this nonfiction section arranged in alphabetical order by the last name of the subject. If more than one biography has been written about a person, then the biographies are put in order by the author's last name.
Ex: *Benjamin Franklin*; d'Aulaire, Ingrid and Edgar Parin
       Meet Benjamin Franklin; Scarf, Maggi
       Benjamin Franklin; Stevenson, Augusta

A **biography** is the story of a person's life written by someone other than that person. An **autobiography** is a person's life story written about himself.

d. Arrange the following biographies in the order you would find them on the library shelf by placing the order number in the space provided.

.... *Susanna Wesley*; Ludwig, Charles

.... *Daniel Webster*; Allen, Robert

.... *George Frideric Handel*; Ludwig, Charles

.... *Robert E. Lee*; Roddy, Lee

.... *Christopher Columbus*; Rhodes, Bennie

4. a. In the General Works section of the library you will find reference books such as encyclopedias. Encyclopedias are arranged in alphabetical order by subject. Each volume has a reference to the range of the alphabet covered in that volume printed on the book for easy reference. For example:

   Ex: Vol. 1 - A to Ameland
         Vol. 2 - Amen to Artillery

   This method allows you to find your subject easily. In an encyclopedia set arranged as listed in the example, in which volume would you find information about the American Revolution? _____

   Which volume would you find information about the Amazon River? _____

   b. Each year a special acknowledgment called the Newbery Award is made to certain books. Use an encyclopedia to answer the following questions about that award.

   1) In what year was the first Newbery Award given? _____
   2) How does a book win this award?

   _____

   _____

   3) Who issues the award?

   _____

   _____

   4) Why was it named "Newbery" Award?

   _____

   _____

   5) What was the title and author of the 1949 award winner? The 1961 award winner? Last year's winner?

   _____

   _____

   _____

6) List some or all of the Newbery Award winners you would like to read.

....

....

Enrichment
Take a trip to the library and find book titles for each letter in the phrase *Library Books*.
Example: L - <u>Little House on the Prairie</u>

L ....   B ....

I ....   O ....

B ....   O ....

R ....   K ....

A ....   S ....

R ....

Y ....

a. Use your library's card file or computer to make a list of all the books your favorite author has written. How many have you read? Would you like to read some other books by this author?

....

....

b. Use an encyclopedia or reference book to find out more information about the author. Ask your librarian if your library owns a book with author information. One such book is called *Something About the Author*.

c. Does the information you found about the author help you determine whether or not the author is a Christian?

....

d. Choose skills from the *Review Activities* on the next page.

Review Activities

1. Refer to your list of library departments to answer the following questions.

   a. In what department would you find a magazine article on nutrition?

   _____

   b. In what department would you find young children's books?

   _____

   c. In what department would you go to locate a video on Spain?

   _____

   d. What department would help you in locating a book?

   _____

2. Use the Dewey Decimal System to classify each of the following books. Write the correct number category next to each selection.

   a. *First Guide to the Universe* _____

   b. *Amazing Machines and How They Work* _____

   c. *Art Through the Ages* _____

   d. *Religions of Many Lands* _____

   e. *World Book Encyclopedia* _____

3. Arrange the following fiction books in the correct order they would appear on the library shelf of fiction by placing the number of their appearance on the space provided.

   a. _____ *Silver for General Washington*, Meadowcroft, Enid

   b. _____ *The Legend of Fire*, Roddy, Lee

   c. _____ *The Bronze Bow*, Speare, Elizabeth George

   d. _____ *Amos Fortune, Free Man*, Yates, Elizabeth

   e. _____ *Gift From the Midado*, Fleming, Elizabeth

Arrange the following biographies in the correct order they would appear on the library shelf by placing the number of their appearance on the space provided. If the book is an autobiography, circle the number.

a. .... *Michael Faraday, Father of Electronics*, Ludwig, Charles

b. .... *Isaac Newton: Mastermind of Modern Science*, Knight, David

c. .... *Inventor, Scientist and Teacher: Isaac Newton*, Tiner, John

d. .... *Ben Carson*, Carson, Ben

e. .... *Martin Luther: Hero of Faith*, Nohl, Frederick

f. .... *The World of William Penn*, Foster, Genevieve

Indicate in which volume you would find the following information.

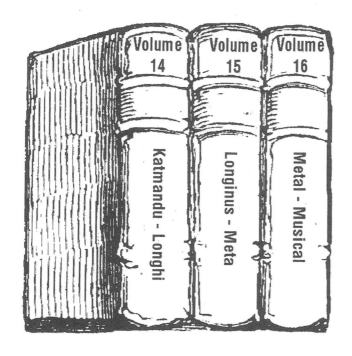

a. Vol. .... - minerals

b. Vol. .... - monarchy

c. Vol. .... - Kitty Hawk

d. Vol. .... - mathematics

e. Vol. .... - library

6. You did some research on the Newbery Award. Another special acknowledgment is the Caldecott Award. Use an encyclopedia or other resource to answer the following questions.

   1) In what year was the first Caldecott award given? ....

   2) How does a book qualify to win the award?

   ....

   ....

   3) What organization issues the award?

   ....

   4) What was the title and author of the 1940 award winner? The 1963 award winner? Last year's winner?

   ....

   ....

   5) Has any one person ever won the Caldecott medal more than once?

   ....

   6) Has any one person ever won both the Newbery and Caldecott Awards?

   ....

   7) For whom was the Caldecott medal named?

   ....

   8) List some of the Caldecott winners you have read.

   ....

   ....

At last either Betsie or I would open the Bible. Because only the Hollanders could understand the Dutch text we would translate aloud in German. And then we would hear the life-giving words passed back along the aisles in French, Polish, Russian, Czech, back into Dutch. They were little previews of heaven, these evenings beneath the light bulb. I would think of Haarlem, each substantial church set behind its wrought-iron fence and its barrier of doctrine. And I would know again that in darkness God's truth shines most clear.

The Hiding Place by Corrie ten Boom.
Used by permission, Chosen Books, 25 Turner Dr., Chappaqua, NY 10514.

a. Copy the literature passage. Compare your copy with the passage and correct any errors.

b. Why are the words French, Polish, Russian, Czech, and Dutch capitalized?

_____

_____

c. Find the word *substantial* in the literature passage. This word contains the prefix **sub-** which means *under*. Add this prefix to your prefix list along with its definition and some word examples.

d. Make a spelling list from any misspelled words from your dictation or use the following list.

aisles	wrought	barrier
substantial	translate	doctrine

_____

_____

_____

e. The word *wrought* is spelled with a silent **w** and **r** to make the /r/ sound.

> **Spelling Tip**
> Some words spell the /r/ sound
> with **wr** as in **write**.

Copy the following words and underline **wr**. Say the words aloud as you write them.

write _____   wren _____   wreath _____

wreck _____   wrestle _____   wrinkle _____

wrong _____   wrap _____

2. a. Read the last two sentences of the literature passage. Discuss with your teacher what you think the author means.

b. The author of this novel is Corrie ten Boom. *The Hiding Place* is the story of her experiences during World War II. Examine the literature passage and determine from what point of view the story is written.

....

c. Although most of the information presented in *The Hiding Place* is based on firsthand experience, the author does present many facts about World War II that she obtained through research.

During the next two weeks, you will research the topic of your choice and write an essay about the subject. When various books, magazines, and other reference materials are used as sources of information for an essay that documents a subject, the resulting paper is referred to as a **research essay.**

Enrichment

Look in the puzzle below and find the spelling words listed in **1d** of this lesson. Look across and down for the words. Circle them.

```
d e l l s u r c o x r
o w r o u g h t u t t
c r j u b s s p g j b
t r a n s l a t e e g
r r r t t a g o e s e
i m i r a r e a a e e
n e l b n i o o i v v
e h o l t c h i s d a
i l o s i b t l l p c
g y o b a r r i e r h
t t w a l l o t s m i
```

a. This lesson will use World War II as a sample topic of research in order to guide you through the process of preparing a research essay.

b. Research requires proper planning. It is important that you follow the steps in the order presented without omitting any steps of research. Keep track of your research planning by using the student checklist at the end of Lesson 19. Each time you complete a step on the checklist, mark the box and move to the next step.

c. Begin your research by first deciding the topic you want to research. Think of a subject you might like to know more about. Then take a trip to your library. Use books, magazines, or an encyclopedia to help you decide on an interesting topic. (Your librarian can help you with any questions you may have.) Your research paper will be only five or six paragraphs so you must narrow down your topic to a specific topic you would like to explore.

Ex: General area of interest: Battles of World War II
        General topic: Battle at Pearl Harbor
        Limited topic: The Destruction of the American Fleet at Pearl Harbor

_____

_____

_____

_____

d. Write a statement of purpose for your essay. This statement is called the **thesis statement** and should express the **main idea** of the essay in a sentence or two. Think of your thesis statement as your focus point. You want your research paper to center around what is said in your thesis statement.

Ex: The destruction of the American fleet at Pearl Harbor had more of an effect on the United States than any other event of World War II.

_____

_____

_____

_____

e. Look back at the Dewey Decimal System in Lesson 17. Write the number or name of the category you would find each of the following books.

_____   a. Books on World War II

_____   b. An encyclopedia

_____   c. A biography of a famous person
                         involved in World War II

f. What section would you find books on the subject of your choice?

_____

g. Spend time today at the library gathering and deciding which books or reference you will use to research your topic. You may include pictures (drawn or otherwise) with your paper. In making your choices include at least one encyclopedia or reference book, one magazine or newspaper (if possible), and one book.

a. Once you have narrowed your broad topic to a more specific topic, begin reading the information you have gathered. Use the index (or subtopics in an encyclopedia) to aid you in your search of specific information. You don't have to read the entire magazine article or book unless you want to. Focus just on the parts that deal with your specific topic.

b. Keep your ideas focused. Make a list of questions on 3 x 5 index cards. For example, with the topic, The Destruction of the American Fleet at Pearl Harbor, you might write the following questions. One question per card.

When did it happen?
Was there warning of an impending attack?
Who fired first?
How was the raid conducted?
Why was timing crucial in the attack?
How many battleships were lost?
What was the cost in human lives?

c. Begin answering your questions on the index cards. Be sure to use your own words. Do not copy information. This is against the law; it is called **plagiarism**. When you use a reference, write where you got your information on the back of the card. You will need this when you make a list of references that goes on the last page of your research paper.

d. Review your spelling words. Remember to be careful of words with silent letters.

e. Continue gathering information and recording it on your note cards.

f. Take an oral or written spelling pretest.

_____

_____

_____

a. Choose one of the following activities. Complete on separate paper.

1) Take the literature passage from dictation again.

2) You may continue to gather information on your note cards.

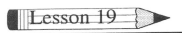

1. a. Now you must put your notes in order. Focus first on your main idea and then follow with details. Look over your note cards and ask yourself these questions.

   ☐ Do all my note cards apply to my subject?
   ☐ Do I need to discard some that do not apply?
   ☐ Do I have enough information on my topic?

   b. Decide what the main points of your essay will be and list them. Group the remaining ideas under these main points forming a **topical outline**. A topical outline uses words or phrases to express ideas; it does not use sentences. The most important points of your outline should be numbered with Roman numerals and the subheadings should be listed by capital letters. Any remaining supporting details should be listed numerically under the subheading they support. Be sure to place a period after each of the numbers and letters used in the outline formation and indent each level. One of the rules used in forming an outline is that you never have just one subheading or just one detail listed under a subheading. You always have at least two subheadings or at least two details. Often this rule is expressed: "You never have an *A* without a *B* and you never have a *1* without a *2*." Look over the following sample topical outline and then create your own outline for the topic you have chosen. Complete on a separate paper.

   The Destruction of the American Fleet at Pearl Harbor

   I. The Japanese Attack on Pearl Harbor

       A. Situation Prior to Attack

           1. U. S. Naval base located on Oahu Island, Hawaii
           2. The bulk of the US fleet was at its base
           3. Japanese diplomats in talks with U.S.
           4. American fleet not on a wartime alert

       B. The Attack

           1. Japanese planes attacked at 7:55 A.M.
           2. First destroyed planes
           3. Second attacked fleet in harbor

   II. U.S. losses at Pearl Harbor

       A. Damage to U.S. Fleet

           1. Battleships: 4 sunk; 4 damaged
           2. Cruisers: 3 damaged
           3. Destroyers: 3 sunk

       B. Lives lost or wounded

           1. Number of Americans killed: 3,581
           2. Number of Americans wounded: 1,168

   III. Results of Battle

       A. Gave Japanese fleet temporary command of Western Pacific
       B. United States enters World War II

a. With your teacher's help review your outline and notes. Pay special attention to any suggestions your teacher makes. Work on an opening paragraph developed from your thesis statement. The **opening paragraph** should contain your thesis statement.

Ex: World War II was raging, but the United States was still attempting to isolate itself from involvement. All this would change early the morning of December 7, 1941. The destruction of the American fleet at Pearl Harbor had more of an effect on the United States than any other event of World War II.

b. Use your outline to continue writing the body of your research paper. This is only your first draft. You may make changes without worrying about being neat. Complete on a separate paper.

a. You must close your research paper. Develop a good **closing paragraph** concluding your research.

Ex: The attack at Pearl Harbor gave Japan temporary command of the Western Pacific. Japan thought it could defeat America before our military forces had time to fight back; instead their attack drew the United States into the war. America had just begun the road to victory.

b. Complete the **first draft** of your research paper. Complete on separate paper.

c. If you choose to include sketches or pictures, neatly mount them onto paper.

d. Ask your teacher to look over your first draft.

a. Discuss your essay with your teacher, and pay special attention to any suggestions that your teacher makes. Review your research essay using a red pencil to make corrections as you check your grammar and spelling. If there are any words you have used too often, use your thesaurus to find synonyms to replace them.

b. In checking over your essay it would be helpful to ask yourself the following questions:

☐ Did I follow my outline?
☐ Did I follow the main idea of my research essay?
☐ Are the opening paragraph and closing paragraph interesting?
☐ Did my thoughts flow well through the paper?
☐ Does it make sense?

c. Using the information on the back of your index cards, make a list of references to go on the last page of your research paper. This list is called a **bibliography.** List only the references you used in your research essay. A bibliography entry should include the author's name (last name first), the title of the book (underlined) or article (in quotation marks), and publication information (state and name of company). Follow the format used in the following example.

Bibliography

Holmes, Richard. <u>The World Atlas of Warfare</u>. New York: Viking Penguin, Inc. *(book)*

"Pearl Harbor Disaster". <u>Collier's Encyclopedia</u>. 1967. *(reference book)*

Jones, Harold. "The Attack of Pearl Harbor." <u>History Chronicles</u> (6, July, 1997): pp 14-18. *(magazine)*

5. Make a neat final copy to give to your teacher. Look over your paper once more. When you are pleased with your work, put your paper in order: outline the research essay, pictures/sketches, and bibliography. A nice way to end your work would be to place it in a folder with the title of your research essay on the front.

Student Checklist

☐ Choose a subject.	☐ Revise first draft.
☐ Narrow topic.	☐ Add sketches or pictures. (optional)
☐ Select research materials.	
☐ Prepare note cards/take notes recording any references used.	☐ Write reference list. (bibliography)
☐ Conduct interview. (optional)	☐ Write final copy.
☐ Write a statement of purpose.	☐ Place in order and put in a folder.
☐ Write an outline.	
☐ Write first draft.	

Assessment 3
(Lessons 12 - 19)

1. Read the following poem. What is its rhyme scheme? _____

When Mother Reads Aloud

When Mother reads aloud, the past
Seems real as every day;
I hear the tramp of armies vast,
I see the spears and lances cast,
I join the trilling fray;
Brave knights and ladies fair and proud
I meet when Mother reads aloud.

When Mother reads aloud, far lands
Seem very near and true;
I cross the desert's gleaming sands,
Or hunt the jungle's prowling bands,
Or sail the ocean blue.
Far heights, whose peaks the cold mists shroud,
I scale, when Mother reads aloud.

When Mother reads aloud, I long
For noble deeds to do --
To help the right, redress the wrong;
It seems so easy to be strong,
So simple to be true.
Oh, thick and fast the visions crowd
My eyes, when Mother reads aloud.

2. Use the verb *lie* correctly in a sentence.

_____

_____

3. Use the verb *lay* correctly in a sentence.

_____

_____

4. What is plagiarism?

5. Find the pronouns in the literature passage in Lesson 9.

6. Write the following singular nouns as plural nouns.

   a. book _____   b. goose _____   c. baby _____

7. Circle the adjectives in the following sentence.

   The ragged, dirty shirt hung on the line.

8. Using your thesaurus, rewrite the above sentence replacing the adjectives with synonyms.

9. Find two articles in the literature passage in Lesson 2.

10. Arrange the following authors' names in alphabetical order.

    Arthur Ransome, Laura Ingalls Wilder, Elizabeth George Speare, Meindert Dejong

1. Arrange the following information in outline form.

Cars, Motorcycles, Places People Live, Condominiums, Apartments, Trucks, Vehicles, Houses

A. _____

   1. _____

   2. _____

   3. _____

B. _____

   1. _____

   2. _____

   3. _____

BOOK STUDY

on

Big Red

Vocabulary

Find each of the following words in the chapters indicated and use context clues to decide the meaning of each word. Then, look up each word in the dictionary and write a definition.

1. ravenous - (Chapter 1) _____

_____

2. profoundly - (Chapter 2) _____

_____

3. careening - (Chapter 6) _____

_____

4. indispensable - (Chapter 9) _____

_____

5. hypodermic - (Chapter 11) _____

_____

Choose the correct word from the words listed above to complete the following sentences.

6. A carpenter's tools are _____ for his work.

7. Mother is _____ against the use of pesticides.

8. The patient grimaced as the doctor placed the _____ in his arm.

9. The race car went _____ into the stands.

10. The young boy had a _____ appetite.

Enrichment

Unscramble these letters to make your vocabulary words.

1. ginreance _____   4. poorfunyld _____

2. neusravo _____   5. iieeabdlnnssp _____

3. medicypodrh _____

Discussion Questions

1. Mr. Haggin entrusts Danny with his valuable dog. What does he see in Danny's character that makes him do this?

2. What are some examples of his character traits found in Chapter 1?

3. Examine your own character. How do you think people see you? What strengths can you identify? What weaknesses?

4. Mr. Haggin explains why people exhibit their dogs. The reason he gives is "he ... will know that he has built on what competent men have declared to be the very best. He will know also that he, too, can go one step nearer the perfection that men must and will have in all things." Is there such a thing as perfection? Why would men seek for perfection?

5. There are two major conflicts between Danny and Ross in the story. Are they resolved? If so, how?

6. Do you think Danny lied to his father about how Red found Ross in the snow?

7. What made Danny change his mind about taking Big Red to hunt Old Majesty?

8. "He was young, but old enough to know that life was seldom easy. And it seemed to him that in the future there would be a great many bears to meet. How he met them depended in great measure on what he did now with Old Majesty." Could Danny have been thinking of something other than real bears that he would have to meet in the future? What kind of bears do you think he meant?

   Can you apply this to your life? In what ways?

9. Danny made the choice to take Mr. Haggin's valuable dog into the forest to meet Old Majesty. What was Mr. Haggin's reaction? Do you think he made the right decision?

10. Foreshadowing in literature is a suggestion of what is to come later in the story by giving hints or clues. What is the major event that is foreshadowed in this book?

Activities

The following activities are intended to help you understand the friendship that Danny and Red formed as well as what Danny's life was like. Choose two or three activities to complete your study. Complete on separate paper.

1. If you have a dog, sign up for dog training classes. These are usually held at community centers or you can call your local veterinarian. Even if you do not have a dog, you can attend these classes and observe the relationship between a dog and his owner.

2. Go to the library or look in the encyclopedia for pictures of different dog breeds. How are dogs grouped? What characteristics determine the different groups?

3. Research the American Kennel Club. What is it? When and why was it formed? What purpose does it serve?

4. Attend a dog show. Talk to the owners and find out what characteristics judges look for in each breed of dog represented.

5. Since money was scarce, Danny and Ross were used to doing things for themselves. For instance, they knew basic first aid and could treat small injuries and illnesses. Think about things around your house that you could do yourself that would save your family money.

6. Ross and Danny made their living hunting and trapping animals. Do you know anyone who hunts? Most hunting today is for the purpose of sport. There are arguments against this as well as arguments in favor. What do you think? Write a paper defending your position.

7. Read other books about Irish setters written by Mr. Kjelgaard, *Irish Red* and *Outlaw Red*, as well as his other books about the wilderness.

I C.A.N. Assessment

for

Big Red - Book Study C

After the *Book Study* is completed, check off each I C.A.N. objective with your teacher.

C   I can **complete** my work.

_____   I can be **creative**.

A   I can be **accurate**.

_____   I can do my work with a good **attitude**.

N   I can do my work **neatly**.

> *The time I spent upon the island is still so horrible a thought to me, that I must pass it lightly over. In all the books I have read of people cast away, they had either their pockets full of tools, or a chest of things would be thrown upon the beach along with them, as if on purpose. My case was very different. I had nothing in my pockets but money and Alan's silver button; and being inland bred, I was as much short of knowledge as of means.*

Kidnapped by Robert Louis Stevenson.

a. Read the literature passage aloud paying close attention to punctuation. Notice the semicolon which joins the two parts of the last sentence. When you read the literature passage, be sure to pause at the semicolon as for a comma. Write the literature passage from dictation, then make any corrections.

_____

_____

_____

_____

_____

_____

_____

_____

_____

_____

_____

b. The main character in the literature passage is also the narrator. What did the narrator in the literature passage think of stories of other castaways?

_____

What emotion or mood does the author create concerning the character's island experience?

_____

Did he have any practical experience in survival or even roughing it?

_____

c. Explain what you think the first sentence of the literature passage means.

d. Make a spelling list from the words you misspelled in your dictation or use the following suggested list:

horrible   either   different   inland   button   knowledge

_____

_____

_____

e. The word *knowledge* is spelled with a silent **k** and **n** to make the **/n/** sound. **Gn** also makes a **/n/** sound. Words may begin with **kn** or **gn**, but **kn** will usually not end a word.

> ### Spelling Tip
> Some words spell the **/n/** sound with **kn** or **gn**; but **kn** will usually not end a word.

Copy the following words and underline **kn** and **gn**. Say the words aloud as you write them.

knee _____	gnaw _____
knight _____	gnat _____
knife _____	gnarl _____
knit _____	reign _____
knock _____	sign _____
knob _____	align _____
knuckle _____	design _____

a. Look at the literature passage again, paying special attention to the pronouns. In which person (first, second, or third) are the pronouns used?

b. Underline the noun that shows possession in the literature passage. How do you know it shows possession?

c. Another method of showing possession is the use of possessive pronouns. **Possessive pronouns** are words that take the place of nouns that show possession. The possessive pronouns most commonly used are:

Commonly Used Possessive Pronouns					
my	mine	his	her	hers	its
your	yours	our	ours	their	theirs

Hint
Possessive pronouns do not use an apostrophe to show possession.

d. Find and list the three possessive pronouns in the literature passage. Beside each one, write what each pronoun is showing possession of.

e. Usually possessive pronouns are used as adjectives in the structure of a sentence. All the possessive pronouns in bold print listed above are used as adjectives.

f. Write the correct possessive pronoun in the space provided in the following sentences.
    Ex: *Mary* went to _her_ Spanish lesson.

    1) *Matthew and Lane* went to _____ favorite fishing spot.

    2) The *car* slowed down to stay in _____ correct lane.

    3) *I* want you to see _____ new shoes.

    4) *Lydia* likes to finish _____ homework before going to softball practice.

    5) *Mike* will achieve _____ goals because he believes in working hard.

g. Being cast away on a deserted island with just money and a silver button would put you
    in a very difficult situation. Think of some things you would need if you were stranded
    on a deserted island. Think about the reasons why you would need those particular
    things. Spend some time talking about it with your teacher to help you clarify your
    thoughts. Put your thoughts on paper and save it for tomorrow's work.

a. **Essays** are used to explain an idea, describe how something is done, argue a point of view, or interpret something you read. In Lessons 18 and 19 you wrote a research essay. Today you will begin work on a different type of essay. It will be an essay in which you express your ideas and views about a survival situation. Use what you wrote in **2g** to guide you in formulating a thesis statement. Place your thesis statement at the top of your outline. This will help you remember to keep your thoughts focused on your main idea.

Ex: Although many items would be useful in a survival situation, I think the three items that would be crucial to my survival would be a knife, matches, and a Bible.

b. The next step in writing an essay is to complete a topical outline in order to better organize your thoughts. First list the three most important items you would need to survive on the island. Each of these main ideas will be numbered with a roman numeral.

c. Under each main idea list at least two reasons why this item would be important to your survival. Note these **supporting details** with a capital letter.

I. Knife

   A. Make weapons for hunting
   B. Cut up food to prepare for eating
   C. Make a shelter

II. Matches

   A. Cook food
   B. Keep warm

III. Bible

   A. Keep from being lonely
   B. Receive comfort from God

d. Any further supporting details should be listed in numerical order under the subheading shown with a capital letter. (See the outline in Lesson 19.) Save your outline for tomorrow.

e. Review your spelling words.

a. Use your outline from yesterday to write the first draft of a short essay. Look over your outline. The first thing you need to do is develop a good opening paragraph. Just as you greet a friend, "Hello!" on the telephone, you must introduce your reader to your idea of the essay. Use your thesis statement as a basis to build your opening paragraph. As you begin your writing, write on every other line. This will make revising your work easier.

b. Now take each main idea and supporting details to form three good paragraphs.

c. You now must close your paragraph. Just as you say, "Goodbye," to a friend as you finish your telephone conversation, you now must conclude your thoughts on paper.

d. Today you have completed a rough draft of your essay. You are building a house, and the bricks are your words! It doesn't need to be perfect. You are working to get your thoughts down in an organized form.

e. Take an oral or written spelling pretest.

5. a. All writers work to get their words just right. Today you will rearrange and add to your rough draft from yesterday. This is the process of editing, revising, and rewriting. This is an important step in writing your essay. Carefully look at each paragraph and decide what you want to change, rearrange, or reword. Perhaps you need to add more details or information.

   b. Use your thesaurus to improve the quality of your words. Doing this will make your writing more interesting and increase your vocabulary.

   c. Check your rough draft for spelling and punctuation. Read your composition aloud. When you are satisfied with the way it sounds, have your teacher check it for grammar, spelling, and content. Write a neat final copy. Complete on separate paper.

   d. Choose one of the following activities. Complete on separate paper.

      1) Write the literature passage from dictation or just take a final spelling test.

      2) Choose skills from the *Review Activities* on the next page.

Review Activities

Underline the possessive pronouns in the following sentences.

a. Their home near the creek is large and roomy.

b. My teacher said I wrote an excellent essay.

c. He grows a variety of different vegetables in his garden.

d. Our family enjoys spending time together.

Arrange the following information in outline form. The title of your outline is: *Eating a Healthy Diet.*

vegetables	foods you should eat	candy
cake	fruit	foods you should avoid
carbohydrates	whole-grain bread	carrots
fried foods	broccoli	apples
fried chicken	high-sugar foods	French fries
peaches	cereal	

September 30. *I was now come to the unhappy anniversary of my landing. I cast up the notches on my post, and found I had been on shore three hundred and sixty-five days. I had kept this day as a solemn fast, setting it apart to a religious exercise, prostrating myself on the ground with the most serious humiliation, confessing my sins to God, acknowledging his righteous judgments upon me, and praying to him to have mercy on me, through Jesus Christ.*

Robinson Crusoe by Daniel DeFoe.

1. a. Copy the literature passage or write it from dictation. Notice the date which begins the paragraph. This is Robinson Crusoe's journal entry for September 30. A **journal** is a record of a person's thoughts and observations. Most entries begin with the date the entry is made.

b. When you complete your dictation, be sure to check your work for any spelling or punctuation errors. Make your spelling list from any misspelled words or use the following suggested list:

judgments	acknowledging	prostrating
humiliation	righteous	religious

c. All of the words in the suggested spelling list have a suffix. Two of the suffixes are **-ion** and **-ous**. The suffix **-ion** means the *act of, state of,* or *result of.* This suffix can also be spelled **-sion** or **-tion**. The suffix **-ous** means *full of* or *having*. This suffix can also be spelled **-ious** or **-eous**. Add each of these suffixes to your list, along with the definition and some word examples.

d. Suffixes make it possible to change a word from a noun to an adjective, from a verb to a noun, and from an adjective to an adverb. Use your list of suffixes to complete the following.
   Ex: Change the noun, *mathematics,* to an adjective meaning *having an ability in mathematics:* mathematical

   1) Change the noun *beauty* to an adjective meaning *full of beauty.*

   _____

   2) Change the verb *inject* to a noun that means *the act of being injected.*

   _____

   3) Change the verb *teach* to a noun that means *one who teaches.*

   _____

   4) Change the adjective *quick* to an adverb that means *in the manner of being quick.*

   _____

e. Some words like *judgments* and *acknowledging* are spelled with **dg** to make the **/j/** sound. The letters **dg** is used only after a single short vowel when making the **/j/** sound.

Spelling Tip
Words are often spelled with **dg** or
dge following a single short vowel
to make the /j/ sound.

f. Copy these words and underline **dg**. Say the words aloud as you write them.

bridge ....   fudge ....

midget ....   edge ....

badger ....   hedge ....

lodge ....

g. How would you describe Robinson Crusoe? Was he happy or unhappy? Can you
determine his relationship to God from the literature passage?

....

....

....

....

....

....

....

2. a. Many people write in journals or diaries to record their thoughts or events in their lives.
Journals are written in the first person because events are being recorded from the
perspective of one of the characters in the story. Look over the literature passage. What
pronouns are used that indicate the passage is written in first person?

....

....

b. Find the word *setting* in the literature passage. The verb *set* means *to place something*. It is often confused with the word *sit* which means *to rest or be seated*. When using the verb *set*, an object should be named that is being placed; the verb *sit* has no object.
   Ex: Please *sit* in this seat.
         Jim *set* his game on the table. (*game* is the object being placed)

c. Complete the following sentences with the correct form of *sit* or *set*.

   1) Will you _____ with me during the concert?

   2) _____ your purse down and stay for a visit.

   3) My dad always _____ in that chair.

   4) Joanna likes to _____ on the beach.

   5) Would you _____ the package on the chair?

d. Pretend you are a historical person who lived long ago. (George Washington at Valley Forge, a Pilgrim on the Mayflower, etc.) Take time today to gather some information on your character and an event which takes place. Jot down notes to use tomorrow.

3. a. Taking the notes you gathered yesterday, create a journal entry for your historical character. Be sure to add enough detail to make it interesting and to understand how the narrator is feeling. Be sure to date your entry.

b. Review your spelling words.

4. a. In the third sentence of the literature passage notice the phrase *prostrating myself on the ground*. The word *on* shows the relationship between the pronoun (myself) and the verb (prostrating). This word is called a preposition. **Prepositions** show the relationship between a noun or pronoun and the other words in a sentence.

A preposition begins a **prepositional phrase**. For example, *on the ground* is the prepositional phrase. *On* is the preposition.

b. Look over the list of some of the most commonly used prepositions.

List of Commonly Used Prepositions				
aboard	at	during	off	under
about	before	except	on	until
above	behind	for	onto	up
across	below	from	outside	upon
after	beneath	in	over	with
against	beside	inside	past	within
along	between	into	since	without
among	beyond	like	through	
around	by	near	to	
as	down	of	toward	

There are fourteen prepositional phrases in the literature passage. Using the list of prepositions, underline the prepositional phrases and circle the prepositions.

c. Complete the following sentences with a preposition.

   1) We will walk _____ Mary's house _____ the sewing class.

   2) Joan's house is _____ the road and _____ the corner.

   3) It is important to be quiet _____ the concert.

d. Take an oral or written spelling pretest.

   _____

   _____

   _____

5. a. Choose one of the following activities. Complete on separate paper.

   1) Write the literature passage from dictation.

   2) Add another entry to the journal you began in **3a**.

   3) Think about how you would feel if you had been marooned on a island by yourself for a year. Write a journal entry telling how you would feel and what you would do on the one year anniversary of your arrival.

   4) Choose skills from the *Review Activities* on the next page.

Review Activities

1. Add the correct suffix to the following words. Following each sentence write what part of speech (noun, verb, adverb or adjective) each new word is.
   Ex: The singer sang a joy<u>ful</u> (*full of*) song. ...adjective...

   a. She lacked the motivat............... (*state of*) to finish the job. ....

   b. The stereo amplifi............... (*that which*) was turned up too loud.
   ....

   c. She is very graci............... (*full of* or *having*) person to allow us to stay in her
   home. ....

   d. The audience applauded loud............... (*like* or *manner of*) at the conclusion of
   the performance. ....

2. Choose the correct form of *sit* or *set* in the following sentences.

   a. She will (*sit, set*) the plant down on the table.

   b. We will (*sit, set*) here for lunch.

   c. Please (*sit, set*) the box down carefully.

   d. Jim likes to (*sit, set*) by the window.

   e. Did you (*sit, set*) my wallet here?

9. Underline the prepositions in the following sentences.

a. The girls walked under the bridge and across the street to the church.

b. The car traveled through the tunnel before reaching its destination.

c. Before you leave, turn off the light beside the door.

d. Beyond this valley is the roadway to the campsite.

e. Until the project is finished we will be inside the house.

Write a journal entry for a day in your own life. Be sure to date the entry and use descriptive words to tell about your day.

"You don't seem to see," continued Toad, "that this fine horse of mine is a cut above you altogether. He's a blood horse, he is, partly; not the part you see, of course—another part. And he's been a Prize Hackney, too, in his time—that was the time before you knew him, but you can still tell it on him at a glance, if you understand anything about horses. No, it's not to be thought of for a moment. All the same, how much might you be disposed to offer me for this beautiful young horse of mine?"

The Wind in the Willows by Kenneth Grahame.

1. a. Look at the first sentence of the literature passage. Notice that this literature passage contains a split quotation. The quotation is interrupted with *continued Toad*. The comma is placed after the first part of the quotation, and after *continued Toad*. The quotation mark will always go outside the comma, period, exclamation mark, or question mark.

b. Copy the literature passage from dictation. Proofread and check your work. Make a spelling list from any misspelled words or use the following suggested list:

altogether	understand	glance
disposed	thought	hackney

....

....

....

c. The word *thought* is spelled with **ough** to make the short **/o/** sound. Most of these words are followed by the letter **t** when making this sound.

> ### Spelling Tip
> Some words like thought are spelled with **ough** to make the short **/o/** sound.

Copy these words and underline **ough**. Say the words aloud as you write them.

bought ....   fought ....   sought ....

brought ....   wrought ....

d. Look up the word *hackney* in the dictionary and find out its meaning and etymology. Is it a word that we would hear used today? Why or why not?

....

e. Make a list of all the contractions you find in the literature passage. Opposite each contraction write the two words that make up the contraction.
Ex: they're - they are

....

....

f. Read the literature passage aloud. Does it sound funny? ....
Do you think Toad really wants to sell his horse?

....

Describe what kind of personality you think Toad would have.

_____

_____

_____

2. a. Look at the fourth sentence of the literature passage. A comma is used to set off introductory words when they begin a sentence. These words are called interjections. An **interjection** is a word or phrase expressing strong or sudden feeling.

Common Interjections
no   yes   well
wow   oh my

An interjection may be separated by a comma or an exclamation mark. Be sure to capitalize the next word if using an exclamation mark.

Ex: Yes, I will help you.
       Wow! Did you see that?

   b. Expressions used in a sentence for emphasis, to set off contrasting ideas, or to indicate an attitude by the speaker are called **parenthetical expressions**. These expressions are independent to the meaning of the sentence, and are set off by commas to separate it from the rest of the sentence. The sentence is independent if it is complete without the expression. Find two parenthetical expressions in the literature passage.

_____

Some of the most commonly used parenthetical expressions are listed below.

Common Parenthetical Expressions	
after all	incidentally
all the same	in fact
as a matter of fact	in my opinion
by the way	naturally
consequently	nevertheless
for example	of course
however	on the other hand
I believe (hope, suppose)	therefore

c. Add commas where needed in the following sentences to set off interjections or parenthetical expressions.

1) Yes I completed my homework before leaving for the game.

2) Natalie on the other hand does not need to practice the piano for a long time to learn a piece.

3) George of course will be happy to go with you.

4) No I was not aware of the change made in your classes.

5) Incidentally the time of the delivery has been changed to 9:00 A.M.

Enrichment
Read each sentence. Fill in the blank with a word that rhymes with the bolded word.

1) The villian on the movie **screen** looked _____.

2) The **plane** was tossed about in the _____.

3) The **boy** broke his new _____.

4) I will take a **look** at the _____.

5) He was very _____ when I began to **panic**.

6) The dog was **sleek** and _____.

7) The **clown** had a big _____ on his face.

8) Mom had to **shake** me three times before I would _____ up.

9) I had a big _____ the other **night**.

a. The literature passage is an example of humorous writing called **irony**. Irony always suggests something different from what is actually said.
   Ex: My doctor said I needed an activity to help calm my nerves so I decided to go skydiving.

As we read the literature passage it is obvious that Toad's horse is not all he claims. What are some clues the author gives us in the passage to help us see this?

_____

_____

_____

b. Try writing a paragraph using the technique of irony. Look at Toad's example. Think of something amusing and make it have the opposite meaning.

_____

_____

_____

_____

_____

_____

c. Review your spelling word for a practice test tomorrow.

Enrichment
Be a Word Detective and decipher the sentence below by filling in the blanks using the clues.

Word List				
bring	not	I	but	did
peace	come	to	a	sword

_____ _____ _____
  1   2   3

_____ _____ _____
  4   5   6

_____, _____ _____
  7   8   9

_____
  10

The clues are on the next page.

Clues:

1) The last word is a weapon.
2) The third word is a negative.
3) The seventh word is a homonym for *piece*.
4) Word two is a palindrome. A *palindrome* is a word that can be read the same, forwards and backwards.
5) The fourth word is the opposite of *leave*.
6) The first and ninth words are the shortest words in the English language.
7) There are two homonyms for the fifth word: *too* and *two*.
8) Words six and eight begin with the same letter.

a. Read the literature passage aloud, pausing for commas and dashes. Add expression and read the passage again as if you were Toad trying to convince someone to buy this horse. Can you envision the humor of this scene?

b. Look at the classified advertisements section of your newspaper. Look over the advertisements for horses and other pets. Male horses are either called *stallions* or *geldings*. A female horse is called a *mare*. If you do not have a newspaper available, use the following example.

FOR SALE: Chestnut Gelding, 12 years old, 14 hands, gentle for anyone to ride. Good-looking horse. $800.
Call 1-437-555-8436 anytime.

Notice that the height of a horse is described in *hands*. Each hand measurement is approximately 4 inches. If a horse is described as being 14 hands, then the horse is approximately 56 inches tall.

c. When you have read a few ads, think of how Toad might describe his horse in a newspaper ad. Write an advertisement for Toad's horse as he might have written it.

d. Take an oral or written spelling pretest.

5. a. Choose one of the following activities. Complete on separate paper.

   1) Write the literature passage from dictation. Compare it with the model and correct any mistakes.

   2) Write another ad for an object you would like to sell. For example, you might write an ad to sell a bicycle, a skateboard, or a dog.

   3) Choose skills from the *Review Activities* on the next page.

Review Activities

1. Rewrite the following paragraph correcting any mistakes in capitalization and adding any needed punctuation.

   yes there are many different breeds of horses continued the instructor some breeds are known for the size and strength of the horses while other breeds are known for their speed.

   _____

   _____

   _____

   _____

   _____

2. Which of the following sentences contain an example of irony? _____

   a. It was a beautiful day, so Marie decided to go to the beach.

   b. The one time Jack arrived at work on time the store was closed.

Before they had gone half a mile, the storm broke with all its strength. Lightning and thunder crashed and flashed together in a perfect fury! Stunned by the force of it, the children ran for shelter under the great oak tree that marked the halfway point between home and school. Its branches lashed and creaked, but it was something sturdy to cling to. Caddie and Warren and Hetty clung together under the tree, but Tom urged them on.

Caddie Woodlawn by Carol Ryrie Brink.
Used by permission, Macmillan Publishing Company.

1. a. Write the literature passage from dictation. Compare your copy to the passage and correct any errors.

Make a list of any misspelled words or use the following list:

strength	lightning	stunned
sturdy	thunder	shelter

_____

_____

_____

b. Look at the spelling words *thunder* and *shelter*. The letter combination **er** is the most common way words make the **/er/** sound. Three other ways to spell the **/er/** sound is **ir**, **ur**, and **ear**.

Copy these words and underline **er**, **ir**, **ur**, and **ear**. Say the words aloud as you write them.

term _____	sir _____	hurt _____	earth _____
serve _____	first _____	purse _____	early _____
fern _____	bird _____	burn _____	learn _____
certain _____	dirt _____	curl _____	pearl _____

c. Underline the prepositional phrases in the literature passage. Circle the prepositions. Review the list of prepositions from Lesson 21 if you need help.

d. Find and draw a box around the possessive pronoun *its* each time it appears in the literature passage. What is the antecedent of *its* in the first sentence of the literature passage? _____

What is the antecedent of *its* in the fourth sentence? _____

e. Find two words in the literature passage with the prefix **be-**. _____
Review your list of prefixes and find their meaning.

f. Using your prefix list, add a prefix to each of the following underlined root words to correctly complete each sentence.

1) If an item is _____ <u>available</u>, it means you will not be able to obtain it.

2) The cat is _____ <u>active</u> if it is sleeping.

3) If you broke the vase, you will have to _____ <u>place</u> it.

4) I hope the weatherman's _____ <u>cast</u> is correct for this weekend.

5) We will _____ <u>port</u> this product for sale in France.

2. a. It is important not to confuse the possessive pronoun *its* with the contraction *it's*. Write two sentences using the words *its* and *it's* correctly.

_____

_____

_____

_____

b. Look at the first sentence in the literature passage.

Before they had gone half a mile, the storm broke with all its strength.

This sentence contains a comma separating a phrase from the remaining sentence.

Read the first part of this sentence: *Before they had gone half a mile.* This phrase does not express a complete thought and cannot stand alone as a sentence. This is called a **dependent clause.**

Now read the second part of the sentence: *the storm broke with all its strength.* This phrase expresses a complete thought and can stand alone as a sentence. This is called an **independent clause**.

When a dependent clause begins a sentence, it is separated from the independent clause by a comma.

Ex: *Although the wind had blown hard*, there was no damage done to the house.

c. Look at the third sentence in the literature passage. Is the first part of the sentence a dependent or independent clause? ....

Is the second part of the sentence a dependent or independent clause? ....

d. Underline the dependent clauses in the following sentences. If the sentence begins with a dependent clause, be sure to place a comma between the dependent and independent clause.

1) Since I started jogging I have been steadily losing weight.

2) If you wish to attend the meeting you must be ready at 9:00 A.M.

3) I will practice playing the piano until I have mastered the skill.

4) When other people have needs we should try to help them.

5) Everyone rejoiced when he arrived home safely.

e. Read the literature passage aloud with expression. Be sure to pause at the commas and emphasize the second sentence of the passage.

f. What do you think will happen next? Write the next sentence as if you were the author.

....

....

....

3. a. Read the literature passage again. Make a list of the things in the order which they happened in the story. When we write about events in the order in which they happened, we are placing the events in correct **sequence**.

      Ex: The storm broke.

              Lightning and thunder crashed and flashed.

....

....

....

....

b. Use your list to tell the story to your teacher. Did you have enough information? ....
Are the events listed in the correct sequence? .... Add to your list if you need to.

c. Using your list, write a paragraph about the literature passage without looking at it. Be sure to write the events in correct sequence. Compare your work with the model. Did you include everything? Are the events in the correct order?

_____

_____

_____

_____

_____

_____

_____

_____

_____

_____

d. Review your spelling words.

Enrichment
Stretch your brain with this logic problem.

    a. Bill has seen *Space Stalker V: Out of Oxygen* two more times than Randy.
    b. Randy has seen the movie three fewer times than Eric.
    c. If Bill has seen the movie thirteen times, then how many times has Eric seen the movie? ....

a. The use of expressive verbs in the writing process allows the writing to come alive for the reader. It can be the difference between the writing being rather drab and uninteresting and being captivating and exciting. Read the following sentences. Decide which of the sentences makes use of expressive verbs.

1) As I walked down the beach, I saw the waves come ashore.
2) As I strolled down the beach, I watched the waves crash ashore.

b. Note that the only difference in the two sentences above is the verbs that were used. Look over the literature passage. What verbs would you consider expressive?

c. Read over the paragraph you wrote in **3c**. Are there any verbs you can change to more expressive verbs? Use a thesaurus to help you find expressive verbs to add to your writing. Edit until you have done your best. Make a neat copy of your paragraph.

d. Take an oral or written spelling pretest.

Enrichment

Read each phrase. Look at the pictures and decide which phrase best describes them. Copy the correct phrase under each picture.

| a circle on a square | a triangle on a rectangle | a square on a triangle |
| a circle on a circle | a square on a square | a triangle on a triangle |

Example:

a square on a triangle

1. _____   4. _____

2. _____   5. _____

3. _____   6. _____

5. a. Choose one of the following activities. Complete on separate paper.

   1) Write the literature passage from dictation. Be sure to use correct punctuation and spelling.

   2) Using the sentence you added to the literature passage in **2f**, continue writing the story as if you were the author. Be sure to make use of expressive verbs.

   3) Choose skills from the *Review Activities* on the next page.

Review Activities

Underline the prepositions. Draw a box around the contraction *it's*. Circle the possessive pronoun *its,* and draw an arrow to the antecedent.

The Privet Hawk Moth hides on tree bark or under leaves during the day, but after the sun sets, it flies around the area looking for nectar. The moth uses its long proboscis to drink nectar from flowers; it's similar to a straw. After the sun rises, the moth grabs onto a tree and remains there until dusk comes again.

Write one sentence with a dependent clause at the beginning of the sentence, and another sentence with a dependent clause at the end of a sentence. Be sure to punctuate the sentences correctly.

_____

_____

_____

_____

_____

_____

Read over the following sentences. Decide the correct sequential order and place the correct order number in front of the sentence. The first one is done for you.

_____ The thaw causes the streams and rivers to swell.

___1___ Spring brings amazing change to the land.

_____ As winter ends, the hours of daylight grow longer and the temperature grows warmer.

_____ Finally, new buds begin to appear on the trees.

_____ The land has completed its change, and a new season has begun.

_____ The increased temperatures cause the winter snows to melt.

_____ As the thaw continues, wildflowers and green grasses begin to bloom.

4. Using a thesaurus, write expressive verbs that could be substituted for the following verbs.

a. sit

b. walk

c. run

d. say

e. see

The Gettysburg Address

The Gettysburg Address

Fourscore and seven years ago our fathers brought forth on this continent a new nation, conceived in liberty, and dedicated to the proposition that all men are created equal. Now we are engaged in a great civil war, testing whether that nation, or any nation so conceived and so dedicated, can long endure. We are met on a great battlefield of that war. We have come to dedicate a portion of that field as a final resting place for those who here gave their lives that that nation might live. It is altogether fitting and proper that we should do this.

But in a larger sense, we cannot dedicate—we cannot consecrate—we cannot hallow this ground. The brave men, living and dead, who struggled here, have consecrated it far above our poor power to add or detract. The world will little note nor long remember what we say here, but it can never forget what they did here. It is for us, the living, rather, to be dedicated here to the unfinished work which they who fought here have thus far so nobly advanced. It is rather for us to be here dedicated to the great task remaining before us,—that from these honored dead we take increased devotion to that cause for which they gave the last full measure of devotion; that we here highly resolve that these dead shall not have died in vain; that this nation, under God, shall have a new birth of freedom; and that government of the people, by the people, for the people, shall not perish from the earth.

Gettysburg Address by Abraham Lincoln.

1. a. Read the text of the *Gettysburg Address*. Carefully look over the bold text portion and write that part from dictation. Compare your dictation copy to the model to see if you made any mistakes. Correct any errors you find.

Make a spelling list from any misspelled words or use the following suggested list:

conceived	portion	endure
proposition	continent	nation

b. Most words spell **/shun/** as in nation with **-tion**. Other words spell it with **-sion**.

> ### Spelling Tip
> Most words spell the **/shun/** sound with **-tion**. Other words spell it with **-sion**.

Copy these words and underline **-tion** and **-sion**. Say the words aloud as you write them.

emotion _____   division _____

lotion _____   lesion _____

caption _____   pension _____

sensation _____   vacation _____

tension _____   vision _____

c. The speech in the literature passage contains a number of prefixes. Find the words that contain the prefixes **con-** and **en-.**

Add these prefixes to your prefix list along with their definitions and word examples. The prefix **con-** means *together* or *with*, and the prefix **en-** means *in* or *into*.

d. Add either the prefix **con-** or **en-** to complete the following words. Use the definitions provided to help you choose the correct prefix.

1) _____compass (*to shut in all around*)

2) _____struct (*to build by fitting parts together*)

3) _____stellation (*a gathering of stars*)

4) _____gage (*to draw into, to involve*)

5) _____gregate (*to meet together*)

2. a. Although the *Gettysburg Address* is a famous speech, there may be several words that you are unfamiliar with. Look up the following words in the dictionary and write a definition for each.

1) conceived _____

2) dedicate _____

3) proposition _____

4) fourscore _____

5) engaged _____

6) endure _____

b. Using the same words from **2a**, use your thesaurus to find synonyms for each word.

_____

_____

_____

_____

_____

c. Look at the bolded part of the *Gettysburg Address* in the literature passage. Rewrite the passage using the synonyms you found in **2b**. Does this help you to better understand the speech?

_____

_____

_____

_____

_____

_____

_____

_____

_____

_____

_____

_____

_____

a. Find the word *their* in the last sentence of the bolded part of the literature passage. The word *their* is a possessive pronoun, but it also has two homonyms. Remember, homonyms are words that sound the same but have a different meaning and usually a different spelling.

Ex: We will travel to *their* house.
      (*Their* is a possessive pronoun.)
      There will be a concert at the park. I will meet you over *there*.
      (*There* is usually an adverb.)
      They're good friends of ours.
      (*They're* is a contraction for they are.)

b. Complete the following sentences with *their*, *there*, or *they're*.

1) _____ are many miles more to travel before we reach our destination.

2) _____ ideas really helped to make this project a success.

3) _____ very surprised they have been chosen to receive the award.

4) The ball flew over _____.

5) _____ dog loves to romp in our yard.

c. The *Gettysburg Address* is a powerful, moving speech. Using an encyclopedia, look under Abraham Lincoln or Gettysburg, and find out some information about the background of the speech. You may use the following questions as a guide.

1) When was the speech made? _____

2) Why was it given?

_____

_____

3) Why is it so powerful and remembered?

_____

_____

4) Where was it given? _____

5) How many copies did Lincoln make of the speech? _____

6) Did Lincoln add anything as he was speaking? (something not on the original draft)

_____

_____

d. Begin to study the *Gettysburg Address*. Plan to have it memorized by the end of next week's lesson. (Only the bolded text portion is necessary to memorize although you can memorize the whole speech if you wish.)

e. Review your spelling words.

a. Take your notes from **3c** and write two to three paragraphs sharing something that you found interesting about the *Gettysburg Address*.

b. Take an oral or written spelling pretest.

_____

_____

_____

Enrichment

Using the letters in Gettysburg Address, make as many little words as you can.

GETTYSBURG ADDRESS

_____

_____

_____

_____

_____

_____

_____

_____

_____

_____

_____

5. a. Write the bolded text portion of the literature passage from dictation. This will also help you to memorize the speech. Check your copy for any mistakes in spelling or punctuation. Complete on separate paper.

   b. Practice saying the bolded portion of the literature passage aloud paying special attention to the punctuation. Be sure to pause for the commas.

a. One method that will help you memorize the *Gettysburg Address* is to prepare index cards with key words or pictures to help you remember specific parts of the speech. For example, you might draw a picture of North America to give you a clue to the word *continent*. After you have finished preparing your cards, number them by placing a small number in the right hand corner. This will help you keep the cards in the correct order.

b. Continue to study and memorize the speech using your index cards.

a. Read the entire *Gettysburg Address* slowly and carefully. Every good speech has several parts: the **introduction**, the **body**, and the **conclusion**. Identify these parts of the *Gettysburg Address* with your teacher.

b. Continue memorizing the speech.

Throughout the week work on the following activities.

Enrichment
Word Detective: Look at the clues below and fill in the blanks to make a famous saying.

Word List								
first	you	try	if	again	try	don't	at	succeed

1 _____ 2 _____ 3 _____ 4 _____

5 _____ 6 _____ 7 _____ 8 _____

9 _____

Clues:
1. Words 7 and 8 are the same word.
2. The 6th word is the opposite of *fail*.
3. The 3rd word comes before *second* in a sequence.
4. The 4th word is a pronoun.
5. The 5th word is a contraction for *do not*.
6. Word 1 and 2 each have 2 letters in them.
7. The 9th word begins with the first letter of the alphabet.

Make up a Word Detective puzzle of your own. Ask someone else to fill in the blanks.

Enrichment

  a. Little Ellie and her friends have fewer books than Little Suzy and her friends.
  b. Little Suzy and her friends have more books than Little Jenny and her friends.
  c. Little Jenny and her friends have twenty more books than Little Ellie and her friends.
  d. Which gang has the most books? _____

3. a. Prepare to make an oral presentation. Use your index cards to practice your speech. Record your speech with a tape recorder, then play it back and listen to yourself. Are there any parts you need to improve?

   b. Follow these guidelines when preparing an oral presentation.

Oral Presentation Checklist
___ 1) Read the speech aloud several times. Try to understand the meaning and the mood of the speech.
___ 2) Use your voice where emphasis is needed and pause accordingly.
___ 3) Speak clearly and loudly. Be sure not to rush through the speech.
___ 4) Look at your audience as if you are speaking directly to them.
___ 5) Stand straight; do not slouch.
___ 6) Practice in front of a mirror.

4. Give an oral presentation of the speech to your group or family. Ask them for any advice as to how you could improve your presentation.

You are now very familiar with the *Gettysburg Address*. Write a paragraph telling about the bolded part of the speech. This will show how well you understand what was said. A retelling of a speech (or any written material) in your own words is called a **paraphrase**.

Ex: Eighty-seven years ago our forefathers formed a new government in this land, based on freedom, etc.

Assessment 4
(Lessons 20 - 25)

1. Rewrite the first two sentences of the literature passage in Lesson 21 as if someone else were telling the story (third person).

2. Write a sentence using *to, two, too*.

3. How are pronouns used?

4. List at least three pronouns that show possession (ex: his).

   Do possessive pronouns ever need an apostrophe?

Rewrite the following phrases using possessive nouns:

a. the book that belongs to John _____

b. the bikes that belong to the boys _____

c. the sister of Pat _____

6. After reviewing the list of common prepositions found in Lesson 21, find three prepositions in the literature passage in Lesson 20.

_____

7. Copy the following sentences and add the correct punctuation:

In fact John said all we have to do is read the directions. I am sure we will be able to build the model by ourselves.

_____

_____

_____

8. Write a word with the prefix **be-**. _____

9. Write a word with the suffix **-tion**. _____

The dog-wanting disease never did leave me altogether. With the new work I was doing, helping Papa, it just kind of burned itself down and left a big sore on my heart. Every time I'd see a coon track down in our fields, or along the riverbanks, the old sore would get all festered up and start hurting again.

Just when I had given up all hope of ever owning a good hound, something wonderful happened. The good Lord figured I had hurt enough, and it was time to lend a helping hand.

It all started one day while I was hoeing corn down in our field close to the river. Across the river, a party of fishermen had been camped for several days. I heard the old Maxwell car as it snorted and chugged its way out of the bottoms. I knew they were leaving. Throwing down my hoe, I ran down to the river and waded across at a place called the Shannon Ford. I hurried to the camp ground.

Where the Red Fern Grows by Wilson Rawls.
Used by permission, Doubleday Books, Dell Publishing Group.

1. a. Read the literature passage. This boy had a "dog-wanting disease" that left a big sore in his heart. Tell your teacher what you think this means.

   _____

   _____

   b. Write the bold part of the literature passage from dictation.

   _____

   _____

   _____

   _____

   _____

   _____

   _____

Check your copy with the passage and make a list of any misspelled words or use the following suggested spelling list:

hoeing	waded	snorted
leaving	chugged	hurried

_____

_____

_____

c. Each of the suggested spelling words has a suffix. Write the root word next to each word. What changes were made in each of the root words in order to add the suffix? Which spelling word is an exception to the rule concerning adding a suffix beginning with a vowel to a root word ending with a silent **e**?

_____

_____

_____

d. Look at the literature passage. List all the words that are capitalized that are not the first word of a sentence or the pronoun *I*. Determine why each word is capitalized. If you are not sure, check with the capitalization rules in Lessons 6 and 16.

_____

_____

_____

2. a. Find the contraction in the first paragraph of the literature passage. Write it as two words.

_____

b. Find the word *its* in the third paragraph of the literature passage. Is it a possessive

pronoun or a contraction? _____

If it is a possessive pronoun, what is its antecedent? _____

c. Read the first sentence of the second paragraph of the literature passage. What do you think happened? Often the author gives us hints as to what is going to happen in the story. This is called **foreshadowing**. What hints do you find in the literature passage that help you to predict what will happen in this story?

_____

_____

_____

_____

_____

_____

d. Write the next paragraph of the story telling what you think happened.

_____

_____

_____

_____

_____

_____

3. a. Looking at the last paragraph of the literature passage, draw a box around all the prepositions. There are nine. If you are unsure of the prepositions, refer to your list of common prepositions in Lesson 21.

b. For each preposition you boxed ask, "What?" Underline the noun that answers that question.

Ex: [in] our <u>field</u>

     Ask yourself, "In what?" In field.

Each word you underlined is called the **object of the preposition**. Some words that are used as prepositions can also be used as other parts of speech. Remember, for a word to be a preposition, it must have an object.

c. Circle the preposition and underline its object in the following sentences.

Ex: We will spend the day swimming ⓐⓣ the <u>pool.</u>

1) Mary delivered fresh bread to her neighbor.
2) I found the novel in the bookcase.
3) We will look for different types of birds by the river.
4) We must travel across the bridge and into the next county.
5) The ball bounced outside the boundary lines.

d. Review your spelling words.

Enrichment

You are in charge of dinner for the next two weeks. Make up a list of meals beginning with each letter in the phrase *Meals for Dinner*.

M _____   D _____

E _____   I _____

A _____   N _____

L _____   N _____

S _____   E _____

                                               R _____

F _____

O _____

R _____

4. a. Have you ever wanted anything as badly as this boy? Did you receive what you wanted?

_____

_____

_____

_____

b. Write a friendly letter explaining your experience to a friend. Follow the format for a friendly letter found in Lesson 5. Be sure to include how you felt. Complete on a separate piece of paper.

c. Take an oral or written spelling pretest.

_____

_____

_____

Enrichment
Use colored paper to make the following.

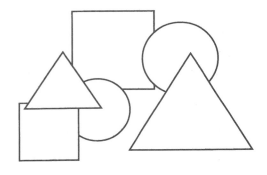

1) a blue circle on a yellow square
2) a green rectangle on a red circle
3) a yellow square on a blue circle
4) a red triangle on a green triangle

5. a. Choose one of the following activities. Complete on separate paper.

1) Write the bolded part of the literature passage from dictation. Were you able to spell all the words correctly? Did knowing the root of a word help you with your spelling?

2) Choose skills from the *Review Activities* on the next page.

Review Activities

1. Add capitalization and punctuation to the following paragraph. Underline any conjunctions.

   in europe during the middle ages falconry or hawking as it was sometimes called was a favorite sport. hawks falcons and eagles were trained to respond to their owners commands and hunt small prey. the bird was hooded and sat on his owners gloved arm. the hood was removed when small game was spotted and the bird would swoop down on its prey. the bird would catch the animal return to his owner with the prey and receive its reward of a piece of meat.

2. Write a paragraph that uses foreshadowing to give the reader a hint of what is going to happen next.

   _____

   _____

   _____

   _____

   _____

   _____

3. Write two sentences that contain a preposition and its direct object.

   _____

   _____

   _____

4. Write a letter to someone that has done something nice for you recently telling that person how much you appreciate it. Complete on a separate sheet of paper.

It was always a pleasure to prowl where fishermen had camped. I usually could find things: a fish line, or a forgotten fish pole. On one occasion, I found a beautiful knife stuck in the bark of a sycamore tree, forgotten by a careless fisherman. But on that day, I found the greatest of treasures, a sportsman's magazine, discarded by the campers. It was a real treasure for a country boy. Because of that magazine, my entire life was changed.

Where the Red Fern Grows by Wilson Rawls.
Used by permission, Doubleday Books, Dell Publishing Group.

1. a. Write the literature passage from dictation.

Compare your copy with the passage and make a list of any misspelled words or use the following suggested list:

sycamore	occasion	magazine
discarded	sportsman	fisherman

Which of the suggested spelling words are compound nouns?

What word is common to both compound nouns?

b. Look at the title of the literature passage. Copy the title paying close attention to the capitalization. Capitalize the first word and every other important word of a title. If handwritten, underline the entire title; if computer generated, use italics.

   Ex: Where the Red Fern Grows - handwritten
         Where the Red Fern Grows - computer generated

c. This literature passage contains the suffix **-less**. Find the word in the passage that contains this suffix. What is the root of this word? The suffix **-less** means *without*. How does the suffix change the meaning of the root word? Add this suffix to your list along with its definition and word examples.

d. Find the prefix **dis-** in the literature passage. This prefix means *apart, take away, reverse*. Add this to your prefix list along with its definition and word examples.

Spelling Tip
When adding a prefix to a word do not add or drop any letters. If the last letter of the prefix and the first letter of the root word are the same, the word will contain a double letter.

Add prefixes to the following root words.

1) dis + satisfied _____   4) im + mature _____

2) dis + appear _____   5) dis + similar _____

3) un + necessary _____

e. Many times a prefix added to a word changes the meaning of the word to mean the opposite. Refer to your prefix list to make words of opposite meaning.
Ex: sufficient (not sufficient) - insufficient

1) necessary (not necessary) _____

2) expensive (not expensive) _____

3) correct (not correct) _____

4) fair (not fair) _____

5) ripe (not ripe) _____

2. a. Look at the first sentence of the literature passage. The subject, *it,* is a singular subject, therefore the singular verb, *was,* is used. A verb must agree with the subject in number. If the subject is singular, then the verb must be singular. If the subject is plural, then the verb must be plural. The following information will help you in determining whether a verb is singular or plural.

Singular Verbs
1) A verb ending in **s** is usually considered singular.
   Ex: He looks. Susan writes. The dog runs.
2) The verbs *am, is, was, does,* and *has* are singular.

Plural Verbs
1) Plural verbs usually do not end in *s.*
   Ex: They look. Susan and Jim write. The dogs run.
2) The verbs *are, were, do,* and *have* are plural.

b. The subject of a sentence determines whether a singular or plural verb is used. Look at the following guidelines for choosing a singular or plural verb.

A singular verb is used when:

1) The subject is singular.
   Ex: The cricket is chirping.

2) The subject is *each, nobody, anyone, everyone, either,* or *neither.* These are singular words.
   Ex: Everyone agrees on your choice.

3) The singular subjects are connected by the words *or* or *nor.*
   Ex: Linda or Mary is babysitting.

4) The subject is a collective noun (one that names a group).
   Ex: My family attends church together.

5) The subject expresses an amount of money.
   Ex: Two dollars is the amount I owe.

A plural verb is used when:

1) The subject is plural.
   Ex: The kittens are cute.

2) The subject is *you.*
   Ex: Are you coming with us?

3) The subjects are connected by *and.*
   Ex: Jim and Tom are working together.

4) Plural subjects are connected by *or* or *nor.*
   Ex: Horses or ponies are fun to ride.

c. Often word phrases separate the subject and verb in a sentence. Do not let these word phrases confuse you when determining subject/verb agreement.

Ex: The *rabbits* in the meadow *eat* the clover.
       (The prepositional phrase *in the meadow* does not affect the subject/verb agreement of *rabbits eat*.)

d. Underline the verb that agrees with the subject in number in the following sentences.

1) Our dog often (*sleep*, *sleeps*) under the porch.

2) The students in the class (*take*, *takes*) their notebooks home.

3) The hummingbird (*drink*, *drinks*) from our feeders.

4) Three dollars (*is*, *are*) the price of admission.

5) Several runners (*is*, *are*) entered in this race.

6) The fish of the coral reef (*was*, *were*) very beautiful.

7) The leaves on this tree (*do*, *does*) not change color in the fall.

8) The members of the church (*pray*, *prays*) for our country.

9) The squirrel outside gathering acorns (*love*, *loves*) to jump through the trees.

10) People (*travel*, *travels*) on this roadway daily.

11) Each of the workers (*was*, *were*) capable of completing the job.

12) Either John or Hank (*is*, *are*) going to drive to the store.

13) (*Has*, *Have*) Martha and Deanna finished the assignment?

14) I hope you (*is*, *are*) coming with us to dinner.

15) Neither the boys nor the girls (*agree*, *agrees*) that the game was played fairly.

e. Capitalize and underline the following titles of books.

1) the princess and curdie _____

2) the house of sixty fathers _____

3) trail of apple blossoms _____

4) the cabin faced west _____

a. Pronouns are used to replace nouns. Find the three different pronouns in the literature passage. ....

b. The literature passage is written in the first person. This means that the author is writing from his point of view, using the pronoun *I*. Most stories, however, are written in the third person, using the pronouns *he, she,* and *they*. Rewrite the literature passage in the third person.
    Ex: It was always a pleasure to prowl where fishermen had camped. He usually could find . . .

c. You have learned to capitalize and underline titles of books. Here is a list of other titles that are also underlined.

    magazines   works of art   movies
    newspapers   music albums   plays
    television programs   ships   trains
    aircraft

d. Capitalize and underline titles in the following sentences.

    Ex: The Gainesville Sun is a source for daily news.
           The *Gainesville Sun* is a source for daily news.

    1) where the red fern grows is an excellent book for young boys and girls to read. (book)

    2) The space shuttle, columbia, is orbiting the earth at this time. (aircraft)

    3) I am cooking a recipe I cut out of the family circle. (magazine)

    4) The doulos will be docking here today. (ship)

    5) Shakespeare's hamlet will be performed by the actors of the Community Theater. (play)

e. Review your spelling words.

a. An adverb describes a verb, adjective, or another adverb. They tell us how, when, where, or to what extent or degree. Find two adverbs in the literature passage.
....

b. Locate the punctuation mark used in the literature passage before the list of things the boy found. This mark is a **colon**. The colon (:) is used to introduce a list. Often the colon is preceded by summary words such as *things, as follows, the following,* or *these.*
    Ex: Be sure to bring the following things: drawing paper, soft lead pencils, and erasers.

c. Colons are also used as follows:

    1) Between the chapter and verse of a Bible reference
       Ex: Romans 10:9

    2) After the salutation of a business letter
       Ex: Gentlemen:

    3) Between the hour and minute when referring to time
       Ex: 2:45

d. Add colons and commas as needed in the following sentences. Remember that items in a series are separated by commas. (Refer to Lesson 10, **3a** if you need further review of this punctuation rule.)

    1) These are the items we need for the trip coolers snacks sleeping bags and sheets.
    2) The meeting will begin at exactly 8 00 P.M.
    3) The children chosen for the team are as follows James Karen Robert Todd and Sandy.
    4) My favorite Scripture verse is II Corinthians 5 17.

e. Pretend you are the young boy described in the literature passage. Write a business letter to *Field and Stream,* 2147 Bird Dog Avenue, Spokane, WA 63458, requesting information on purchasing a hunting dog. This letter will not be mailed; it is only for the purpose of acquainting you with the format of a business letter. Use the model on the next page as an example for your letter. The parts of the business letter are labeled in italics for your information. Do not copy these words when you are writing your letter.

f. Take an oral or written spelling pretest.

(Heading)
1234 Main Street
Seattle, WA 63782
September 8, 1997

(Inside Address)
Field and Stream
2147 Bird Dog Avenue
Spokane, WA 63458

(Salutation or Greeting)
Gentlemen:

(Body)
I read your article on purchasing hunting dogs in the August edition and would like to have the additional information you offer along with the list of breeders. Please send this information to me at the address listed below:

Mr. James Harris
1234 Main Street
Seattle, WA 63782

Thank you for your attention in this matter.

(Closing)
Sincerely,

(Signature)
James Harris

5. a. Choose one of the following activities. Complete on separate paper.

    1) Write the literature passage from dictation and check your copy.

    2) Write a paragraph describing your favorite magazine. Use adverbs to help describe why you find it so interesting. Remember to underline the title of the magazine and capitalize the first word and every important word in the title.

    3) Choose skills from the *Review Activities* on the next page.

Review Activities

Add a suffix from your list of suffixes to the following root words to fit the definition given. If you are not sure about a word, check your dictionary.

a. heart_____ (*without heart or compassion*)

b. thank_____ (*full of thanks*)

c. quick_____ (*manner of quick*)

d. connect_____ (*the state of being connected*)

e. paint_____ (*one who paints*)

2. Add the prefixes to complete the following words.

a. dis + solve _____   d. un + written _____

b. im + material _____   e. un + navigable _____

c. im + practical _____

3. Choose the correct verb to complete the following sentences:

a. Everyone (*is, are*) going to the lecture tonight.

b. The panther (*run, runs*) swiftly through the underbrush.

c. (*Do, Does*) Rick and Mary know where to meet us?

d. James or John (*has, have*) the skill to play the piano.

e. The paintings on the wall (*contain, contains*) beautiful colors.

4. Read each of the following sentences. Indicate whether the sentence is written in first (**1**), second (**2**), or third person (**3**). Underline the pronouns that help you in making your decision.

a. _____He drove into the placid pool of water and broke through the surface of the water with a shout.

b. _____I ran as I had never run before; my lungs were ready to burst.

c. _____You must pay attention if you hope to succeed in mastering this skill.

263

5. Capitalize and underline the titles in the following sentences.

   a. The miami herald printed a story about the many boating accidents in their area. (*newspaper*)

   b. little women is based on the life of author, Louisa May Alcott. (*book*)

   c. The mona lisa is on display at the Louvre in Paris. (*painting*)

   d. I read an article about the future of the economy in time. (*magazine*)

   e. The television program, christy, is based on the novel by Catherine Marshall. (*television program*)

6. Add colons to the following sentences.

   a. We will begin hiking the trail at 800 A.M.
   b. The pastor based his message on Romans 10 9.
   c. The following things were littering the ground cans, newspapers, and bottles.
   d. You will be taking these subjects this fall science, literature, and algebra.

7. Write a business letter to the company of your choice. Use the space provided on the next page.

8. Add punctuation and capitalization in the following paragraph.

   what do you feel is our nation's greatest resource water is the greatest natural resource our country has we most often think of water in terms of drinking water and water for household needs there are many other ways that water is valuable some of these uses are as follows transportation irrigation and hydroelectric power the united states would not be the rich nation it is today without the ability to transport its goods down the mississippi river or use the waters of the colorado river to water farmland in the west much of the electrical power in the west is generated by hydroelectric power plants no other natural resource is as valuable to our nation as our water supply

It was almost quite dark, the girls were getting tired, and as Bobbie said, it was past bedtime, when suddenly Phyllis cried, "What's that?"
And she pointed to the canal boat. Smoke was coming from the chimney of the cabin, had indeed been curling softly into the soft air all the time—but now other wreaths of smoke were rising, and these were from the cabin door.
"It's on fire—that's all, " said Peter, calmly. "Serve him right."
*"Oh—how **can** you?" cried Phyllis. "Think of the poor dear dog."*

The Railway Children by E. Nesbit

1. a. Read the literature passage paying close attention to how quotation marks are used. Written conversation is called **dialogue**.

   b. The last part of the literature passage is a conversation. When writing dialogue, begin a new paragraph when there is a change in speaker.

   c. Write the literature passage from dictation.

Proofread and correct your work. Make a spelling list from the words you misspelled or use the following suggested list:

bedtime	chimney	wreaths
suddenly	pointed	softly

d. Some words, like *chimney* are spelled with the ending **ey**. Other words, like *candy* are spelled with just **y**. It is helpful to know the correct spelling of these words so you can spell the plural form correctly.

To form the plural of words ending with a consonant before the **y**, change the **y** to **i** and add **es**. To form the plural of words ending with a vowel before the **y**, just add **s**.

Ex: chimney - chimneys
      candy - candies

Spelling Tip
To form the plural of words ending
in y preceded by a consonant,
change the **y** to **i** and add **es**.
Otherwise, just add **s**.

e. Copy these words and write their plural forms.

chimney _____   monkey _____   donkey _____

candy _____   pony _____   sky _____

f. Which words from the suggested spelling list are used as adverbs in the literature passage?

_____

What suffix helps to identify these words as adverbs? _____

2. a. Locate the word *poor* in the literature passage. What does this word mean?

_____

The word *poor* has two meanings. If you are unsure, look the word up in the dictionary. The word *poor* also has two homonyms (words that sound the same but have different meanings and spellings). The homonyms are *pore* and *pour.* Look up the meanings in the dictionary for each of these words.

_____

_____

You will find the word *pore* also has two definitions. Write one sentence for each homonym.

_____

_____

_____

_____

_____

_____

b. Note the dashes (—) in paragraphs two, three, and four. What other punctuation mark could be used instead to tell the reader to pause in these places? While a dash can be used to indicate a pause or break in thought, it also is used to emphasize and set apart a word or phrase. Sometimes a dash is used to indicate an interruption in speech by another person.
Ex: There is something-actually many things—that we need this afternoon. (break in thought)

At this meeting—this private meeting—we will discuss plans. (emphasis)

Hello—no, I'm sorry—I'm afraid we won't be.

c. Look at the last sentence in the literature passage. Since both a dash and a comma causes the reader to pause, a comma could replace the dash following *Oh*. Words like *oh* used at the beginning of a sentence to express strong emotion or a sudden feeling are called **interjections**. Usually a comma or an exclamation point follows an interjection. If a comma is used, do not capitalize the next word; if an exclamation point is used, remember to capitalize the next word.

Ex: Well, I hope my cousins come to visit this year.
          Oh! What a pretty dress!

Write two sentences; one using an interjection followed by a comma and another using an exclamation point.

d. Look at the word *can* in the first sentence of the last paragraph in the literature passage. It is printed in a different type for emphasis. Try reading the literature passage aloud using good expression.

e. The way we emphasize words can change the entire meaning of a sentence. Try reading the literature passage again, emphasizing different words. For extra fun, try taping your reading on an audio tape.

. a. What do you think about Peter's attitude?

Let your imagination take you to the scene depicted in the literature passage. What would you tell Peter?

b. Write what you think happened next. Be sure to write it in conversational form (dialogue) and remember to use quotation marks around all direct quotations. Everytime someone different is speaking make sure you indent. You can review the quotation rules in Lesson 7.

_____

_____

_____

_____

_____

_____

c. Quotation marks are also used around the titles of songs, short stories, chapters of a book, magazine articles, and short poems. Capitalize the first word and every other important word.
Ex: "The Eagle" (short poem)
         "A Mighty Fortress" (song)
         "The Gift of the Magi" (short story)

d. Add quotation marks and punctuation to the following sentences.
Ex: You must go with us to the museum said James
         "You must go with us to the museum," said James.

1) Which dog is best for a pet in an apartment asked Jim

2) If you will come with me pleaded Myra we will ask Mrs. Jimson together

3) There are many ways to solve the problem said Kelly

4) Run quickly or they will catch you exclaimed Janice

5) The teacher assigned the poem The Charge of the Light Brigade to read for discussion in class tomorrow

e. Review your spelling words.

4. a. Pretend you are a television reporter sent to get the "scoop" on a fire. Write out your report on separate paper, being sure to include the four essential information points of any news article.

    1) Who is the story about?   3) When did the story take place?
    2) What is the story about?   4) Where did the story take place?

  b. Once you have completed your report, practice saying it aloud. Use a cassette recorder or video camera to record your version of the news report.

  c. Take an oral or written spelling pretest.

Enrichment
Read the following sentences one time. Then close the book and draw a picture on a separate sheet of paper of what you read. Reread the sentences to check your picture.

    A white and black cat tried to climb the tree. There on the top limb of the tree sat a blue bird. I wonder if the cat will get the bird.

5. a. Choose one of the following activities. Complete on a separate sheet of paper.

    1) Write the literature passage from dictation. Proofread and make any corrections. If you still have questions about the use of quotation marks, ask your teacher to explain.

    2) Try acting out the literature passage plus the part you added in **3b**.

    3) Choose skills from the *Review Activities* on the next page.

Review Activities

1. Underline the correct homonym in each of the following sentences.

   a. He used (*pore, pour, poor*) judgment in choosing a fishing spot.

   b. Please (*pore, pour, poor*) yourself some lemonade.

   c. The sweat flowed from every (*pore, pour, poor*) of his body.

   d. He will often (*pore, pour, poor*) over old documents at night trying to unlocked their secrets.

   e. The (*pore, pour, poor*) cat looked terrible after falling into the puddle.

2. Underline the interjections and add punctuation at the end of each sentence.

   a. Oh What a lovely dress

   b. Well so you did decide to come

   c. Hurrah We won the championship

   d. My what a lovely daughter you have

   e. Behold I stand at the door and knock

The *Review Activities* continue on the next page.

. Rewrite the following sentences of dialogue. Begin each new paragraph by indenting, and add quotation marks and punctuation where needed. Be sure to punctuate any interjections.

      Mary it was a great concert last night exclaimed Ginger. I wish you could have come. Well it was hard to stay home and babysit last night, but I had already promised Mrs. Wilson I would watch her children while she went to a meeting said Mary with a shrug. How many in the youth group came? Everyone came but Sam and John answered Ginger. The band sang my favorite song. It was great! Oh well I sat around and read in Horses magazine sighed Mary but I know I made the right decision to be faithful to my promise.

4. Write a news report about something that has happened in your life. It could be about a sport, a trip, a concert, an accomplishment, etc. Be sure to include the who, what, when and where points in your story.

Give thanks to the Lord, for He is good;
For His lovingkindness is everlasting.
Give thanks to the God of gods,
For His lovingkindness is everlasting.
Give thanks to the Lord of lords,
For His lovingkindness is everlasting.
To Him who alone does great wonders,
For His lovingkindness is everlasting;
To Him who made the heavens with skill,
For His lovingkindness is everlasting;
To Him who spread out the earth above the waters,
For His lovingkindness is everlasting;
To Him who made the great lights,
For His lovingkindness is everlasting:
The sun to rule by day,
For His lovingkindness is everlasting,
The moon and stars to rule by night,
For His lovingkindness is everlasting;

To Him who smote the Egyptians in their first-born,
For His lovingkindness is everlasting,
And brought Israel out from their midst,
For His lovingkindness is everlasting,
With a strong hand and an outstretched arm
For His lovingkindness is everlasting;
To Him who divided the Red Sea asunder,
For His lovingkindness is everlasting,
And made Israel pass through the midst of it,
For His lovingkindness is everlasting;
But He overthrew Pharaoh and his army in the Red Sea,
For His lovingkindness is everlasting;
To Him who led His people through the wilderness,
For His lovingkindness is everlasting;
To Him who smote great kings,
For His lovingkindness is everlasting,
And slew mighty kings,
For His lovingkindness is everlasting:
Sihon, king of the Amorites,
For His lovingkindness is everlasting,
And Og, king of Bashan,
For His lovingkindness is everlasting,
And gave their land as a heritage,
For His lovingkindness is everlasting,

275

Even a heritage to Israel His servant,
For His lovingkindness is everlasting;

Who remembered us in our low estate,
For His lovingkindness is everlasting,
And has rescued us from our adversaries,
For His lovingkindness is everlasting;
Who gives food to all flesh,
For His lovingkindness is everlasting,
Give thanks to the God of heaven,
For His lovingkindness is everlasting.

Psalm 136:1-5 (NASB).

1. a. Look over the literature passage. Read the literature passage aloud with your teacher. Alternate reading the lines with your teacher, saying the chorus together. This type of reading is called **choral reading.**

   b. This poem is from the book of Psalms in the Bible. Psalms is the songbook of the Bible; it contains poems that were sung. Some of the things they express are praise to God, confessions of fear or sin, and thanksgiving. Read a few psalms with your teacher and discuss the reason you think each psalm was written.

   c. Look at the bolded text of the literature passage and notice the punctuation and where it is indented. Write the bolded portion of the literature passage from dictation. Correct your copy.

d. Make a spelling list from any misspelled words or use the following suggested list:

lovingkindness   everlasting

Both of the suggested spelling words are compound words. Divide them into the two words that make up each of the words.

e. Find the suffix **-ness** in the literature passage. This suffix means *state of.* Add this suffix to your list along with its definition and word examples.

> ### Spelling Tip
> When adding a suffix beginning with a consonant, such as **-ness** or **-ly**, do not drop or change any letters in the root word unless the word ends in **y**. If the last letter of the root word and the first letter of the suffix are the same, double letters will result. If a word ends in **y**, change the **y** to **i** before adding any suffix except **-ing**.

Ex: final + ly = finally
         happy + ness = happiness
         hurry + ing + hurrying

f. Add suffixes to the following words.
Ex: stubborn + ness = stubbornness

1) natural + ly _____

2) sudden + ness _____

3) date + less _____

4) rude + ly _____

5) weak + ness _____

2. a. Look at the first line of the literature passage. The verb is *give*.

What is the subject? _____

Identify the type of sentence: declarative, interrogatory, imperative, or exclamatory.

_____

Refer to Lesson 8 for information on the four types of sentences if you need help.

b. Determine whether the following sentences are declarative (**Dec**), interrogatory (**Int**), imperative (**Imp**) or exclamatory (**Exc**).
Ex: <u>Dec</u>   I like to read biographies.

_____ 1) Open a biography and look into the life of a famous person.

_____ 2) What is the purpose of reading a biography?

_____ 3) A biography helps us to identify what character qualities helped to make that person great.

_____ 4) A biography helps us also to see a period of history through the viewpoint of a person who lived during that time.

_____ 5) It's a great way to study!

c. Just as God was good to Israel, He is good to you. List some ways He is good to you.

_____

_____

Enrichment
Word Detective: Look at the clues below and fill in the blanks to make a famous saying.

Word List							
better	it	than	to	is	to	receive	give

_____   _____   _____   _____

   1   2   3   4

_____   _____   _____   _____

   5   6   7   8

The clues are on the next page.

Clues:

1) The 2nd word is a *be* verb.
2) The 3rd word is the comparative word for *good*.
3) The 4th and 7th words are the same word.
4) The 1st word is a pronoun.
5) The 8th word follows the spelling rule: *i before e except after c.*
6) The 5th word is the opposite of the 8th word.
7) The 6th word begins like the word *there*.

a. Not all poetry rhymes. The selection of the words and how they are placed in a line, or the pattern of sound and words are important. What do you notice about every other line

of the poem? ....

This is a technique called **repetition.**

b. Psalm 136 is a psalm of praise. Try writing a poem of praise to God using the technique of repetition. You can even use the same repetitive line used in Psalm 136. The alternate lines should state truths you know about God or tell of great deeds He has done. Use the list you wrote in **2c** about how God is good to you for some ideas.

_____

_____

_____

_____

_____

_____

_____

c. Review your spelling words.

Enrichment
Use a clock or watch to see how long it takes you to do the following:

Say the alphabet. _____

Flip a coin and get heads 15 times. _____

Count from 100 to 1. _____

Find the word *quick* in the dictionary. _____

Say "Peter Piper picked a peck of pickled peppers" five times with no mistakes. _____

4. a. Verbs change their form in order to show the time of action. These forms of verbs are called **tenses**. A verb may be written in present, past, or future tense.
   Ex: I stand here now. (present tense)
          I stood here yesterday. (past tense)
          I will stand here tomorrow. (future tense)

   b. Find examples of verbs in the present tense and in the past tense in the literature passage.

   _____

   _____

   _____

   c. Most verbs are changed to past tense by adding the suffix **-ed** to the verb. These are called **regular verbs**. If a verb changes in some other way or makes no change to form the past tense, then the verb is called an **irregular verb.**

   Regular verb:
   She arrives on time everyday. (present tense)
   She arrived on time today. (past tense)

   Irregular verb:
   I swim often at the pool. (present tense)
   I swam at the pool. (past tense)

d. Find seven examples of irregular verbs in the literature passage and underline them.

_____

_____

e. It is important to select one tense and use that tense consistently throughout your writing and not switch to another tense.

Ex: Mary jumped up and hits the ball over the net.
         (*Jumped* is past tense; *hits* is present tense.)

         Mary jumps up and hits the ball over the net.
         (Both *jumps* and *hits* are in the present tense.)

f. Read the following paragraph. Change any necessary verbs so that the text reads consistently in the past tense.

It was a beautiful morning, and Echo gallops for joy across the pasture. She stretches her long neck over the fence so she had a better view of the farmyard activities. The chickens clucked loudly from the henhouse as they lay their morning eggs. Bessie, the cow, moos from her barn stall as she waited to be milked. The barnyard cat chased a mouse around the corner and soon returns with it dangling by its tail. With his usual air of importance the proud rooster strutted into his position on the rickety fence post and crows as a signal to all that the day has begun.

g. Take an oral or written spelling pretest.

_____

_____

_____

_____

_____

5. a. Choose one of the following activities. Complete on separate paper.

    1) Write the bold portion of the literature passage from dictation again, or have your teacher continue dictating the remaining verses from Psalm 136.

    2) Find the following words in the literature passage: *asunder*, *adversaries*, *heritage*, *smote*, and *slew*. Tell your teacher the meaning of each of the words. If you are unsure of their meanings, look them up in the dictionary. Write a sentence for each word using it correctly.

    3) Discuss with your teacher the difference in mood of Psalm 136 and Psalm 42.

    4) Choose skills from the *Review Activities* on the next page.

Review Activities

1. Using your list of suffixes add a suffix that matches the definition given to the following words.

Ex: the state of being sad = sadness

a. in the manner of the usual = usual_____

b. the state of being mean = mean_____

c. without care = care_____

d. the act of subtracting = subtract_____

e. one who dives = div_____

2. Write an example of each of the following types of sentences: **declarative**, **interrogatory**, **imperative**, and **exclamatory**.

3. Write a poem using the technique of repetition.

_____

_____

_____

_____

_____

_____

_____

4. Write the correct tense of the verb indicated in parentheses.

   a. I _____ the essay tomorrow. (future tense of *write*)

   b. The hummingbirds _____ quickly from flower to flower. (present tense of *fly*)

   c. The young boy _____ over the fence. (past tense of *jump*)

5. Write the past tense of each of the following verbs and indicate whether the verb is regular (**R**) or irregular (**IR**).
   Ex: freeze - froze (IR)

   a. blow _____   d. take _____

   b. lose _____   e. wave _____

   c. fill _____   f. draw _____

Red took three uncertain steps forward and stopped again. *Danny rushed angrily toward him. He reached down to grasp Red's collar, but the toes of his snowshoes crossed and he stumbled forward again. His bare hands plunged deeply into the snow. They hit something soft and yielding, something that gave before them. It was a man's trousered leg. Danny dug frantically, and lifted Ross Pickett from his snowy bed. His hand went under Ross's shirt. His father was warm and his heart still beat.*

Big Red by Jim Kjelgaard.
Copyright 1945. Renewed 1973, Edna Kjelgaard.
Reprinted by permission Holiday House.

1. a. Look over the literature passage making note of punctuation and spelling, and then write the passage from dictation. Proofread your copy and correct any errors in punctuation and spelling.

b. Make a spelling list of any misspelled words or use the following suggested list:

angrily   snowshoes   stopped
yielding   frantically   trousered

c. What spelling rule applies to the word *angrily*?

What spelling rule applies to the word *stopped*?

d. Find the word *frantically* in the literature passage. When a word ending in **ic** is an adjective, the adverb is usually formed by adding **-ally** rather than just **-ly**.
Ex: energetic - energetically

e. Add the suffix **-ally** to the following words.

1) pathetic

2) realistic

3) enthusiastic

f. Underline the words in the literature passage that show ownership. What has been added to each of these words to show they are possessive?

2. a. Find and circle all the words in the literature passage that end with the suffix **-ly**. These words tell *how, when, where, how often* or *to what extent*. Note that although most words ending in **-ly** are adverbs, some are adjectives, such as *friendly* and *lovely*. If you need to review adverbs, refer to Lesson 5.

b. Draw an arrow from the adverbs you have circled to the verb it tells about. Tell your teacher what each adverb tells about the verb.

    Ex: Danny rushed (angrily) toward him.
               (The adverb *angrily* tells how he rushed.)

c. Not all adverbs end in **-ly**. Adverbs modify not only verbs, but sometimes adjectives or other adverbs.

    Ex: The car sped around the curb (too) rapidly.
               (The adverb *too* is modifying the adverb *rapidly*.)

               The players were (very) happy after winning the game.
               (The adverb *very* modifies the adjective *happy.)*

Look at the literature passage. Find four adverbs that do not end in **-ly** and indicate the verb being modified.

d. Write four sentences using adverbs to answer how, when, where, how often, or to what extent.
    Ex: The rabbit hopped *merrily* through the field. (how)
               The plumber called *yesterday*. (when)
               The toddler fell *down*. (where)
               Mother is *very* happy. (to what extent or degree)

3. a. Every verb has four principal parts: the **present**, the **present participle**, the **past**, and the **past participle**.
    Ex: present - look
               present participle - (is) looking
               past - looked
               past participle - (have) looked

Note that the present participle and past participle are used with helping verbs such as *is, are, am, have, has, had,* etc.

b. Regular verbs form the past and past participle by adding **-ed** to the present form. The present participle is formed by adding **-ing** to the present form. Write the principal parts of the following regular verbs.

	Present	**Present Participle**	**Past**	**Past Participle**
Ex:	1) change	changing	changed	(have) changed
	2) ask			
	3) fill			
	4) love			
	5) rush			
	6) climb			

c. Irregular verbs form the past and past participle in different way... Because there is no single rule that applies to irregular verbs, it is important to familiarize yourself with them. Look at the following list of the most common irregular verbs. The present participle form has not been included in the list because it is always formed by adding **-ing** to the present form.

Irregular Verbs

Present	**Past**	**Past Participle**
beat	beat	(have) beaten or beat
become	became	(have) become
begin	began	(have) begun
bite	bit	(have) bitten
blow	blew	(have) blown
break	broke	(have) broken
bring	brought	(have) brought
burst	burst	(have) burst
catch	caught	(have) caught
choose	chose	(have) chosen
come	came	(have) come
creep	crept	(have) crept
do	did	(have) done
draw	drew	(have) drawn
drink	drank	(have) drunk
drive	drove	(have) driven
eat	ate	(have) eaten

Present	Past	Past Participle
fall	fell	(have) fallen
fight	fought	(have) fought
fly	flew	(have) flown
forget	forgot	(have) forgotten
freeze	froze	(have) frozen
get	got	(have) got or gotten
give	gave	(have) given
go	went	(have) gone
grow	grew	(have) grown
hang	hung	(have) hung
know	knew	(have) known
lay	laid	(have) laid
lead	led	(have) led
leave	left	(have) left
lie	lay	(have) lain
lose	lost	(have) lost
pay	paid	(have) paid
ride	rode	(have) ridden
ring	rang	(have) rung
rise	rose	(have) risen
run	ran	(have) run
say	said	(have) said
see	saw	(have) seen
set	set	(have) set
shake	shook	(have) shaken
shine	shone, shined	(have) shone, shined
shrink	shrank	(have) shrunk
sing	sang	(have) sung
sink	sank	(have) sunk
sit	sat	(have) sat
speak	spoke	(have) spoken
spring	sprang	(have) sprung
steal	stole	(have) stolen
swear	swore	(have) sworn
swim	swam	(have) swum
swing	swung	(have) swung
take	took	(have) taken
tear	tore	(have) torn
think	thought	(have) thought
throw	threw	(have) thrown
wear	wore	(have) worn
weep	wept	(have) wept
win	won	(have) won
weave	wove	(have) woven
write	wrote	(have) written

d. Underline the verbs in the literature passage. What is the tense of each verb?

Remember to watch for helping verbs that indicate past participle. Also indicate which of the verbs are irregular.

How can you tell?

e. Complete the following sentences with the correct verb form.
Ex: *come* She <u>came</u> from India to study in our country.

1) We have .... *(do)* the majority of the work for this project.

2) I .... *(choose)* this subject for my experiment because it was interesting.

3) They .... *(leave)* church early because Joshua did not feel well.

4) Jeremiah had .... *(think)* over his plans for the future carefully.

5) They .... *(build)* the house for a family whose house had burned down.

6) Have we .... *(buy)* enough supplies for the trip?

7) Only a few people have .... *(swim)* that distance.

8) We have .... *(speak)* to Hannah about becoming a member of our Bible Quiz Team.

9) The garden .... *(grow)* quickly in the summer heat.

10) She .... *(take)* the letter to the post office to purchase a stamp.

f. Review your spelling words.

a. Imagine you work for your local newspaper. You have been assigned to report what happened to Danny and his father. A news story should be written in a short, crisp, direct form. Use your imagination and make up your own details to create a newspaper account of this story. Complete on separate paper. Follow these guidelines:

1) The first paragraph of a story usually has very important information in it. It answers the questions *who, what, when,* and *where*.

2) The other paragraphs in the story usually tell why something has happened and how it happened. These paragraphs usually have details about the event. Sometimes quotes from the people involved are included.

Read some newspaper articles to see how they organize their information. Read the following example.

Snowy Town - On Saturday, Ross Pickett, his son, Danny, and their dog, Red, went on a cross country trek across the Snowy Mountain Banks. Little did they know that by Sunday afternoon, Danny and Red would be heroes.

Authorities say circumstances are still unclear as to what took place. However, it is known that Ross and Danny became separated just as an unexpected blizzard came upon them. Danny told authorities that as he searched for his father, Red insistently nudged him in the opposite direction. Danny tried to pull Red the other way, but he lost his footing and fell down. As his hands reached down into the snow, he felt a man's trousered leg. Frantically, Danny dug and lifted his father from the snowy bed. "I put my hand under his shirt, and he was warm and his heart still beat," Ross said with joyful tears, as he lay recuperating in his bed.

Father and son are in good condition at Hope Hospital. Red is in excellent health, enjoying his new found attention.

b. Create a headline for your story that will catch the attention of the reader.

c. Take an oral or written spelling pretest.

Enrichment

List the four people in order from shortest to tallest.

    a. Melissa is taller than Sally.
    b. Melissa is shorter than John who is taller than Sally.
    c. Sally is taller than Albert.
    d. Albert is shorter than John.

_____ _____ _____ _____

5. a. Choose one of the following activities. Complete on separate paper.

    1) Write the literature passage from dictation. Proofread and correct any errors in punctuation and spelling.

    2) Use your thesaurus to revise your news story. Edit carefully. Be sure to use good descriptive words. Rewrite it neatly and give it to your teacher.

    3) Choose skills from the *Review Activities* that follow.

Review Activities

1. Look at the following words and decide if you add the suffix **-ly** or **-ally** to form the adverb.

    a. basic _____   d. drastic _____

    b. serious _____   e. eager _____

    c. sweet _____

2. Circle the adverbs in the following sentences. Write the question the adverb answers: *how*, *when*, *where*, *how often*, or *to what extent*.
Ex: The German shepherd ran (swiftly) beside the bicycle. how

    a. The keys were found inside the car. _____

    b. We will be attending the concert today. _____

    c. We often take a walk after dinner. _____

    d. Laura laughed cheerfully at the joke. _____

    e. He is very concerned about his test scores. _____

Underline the correct verb form in the following sentences. Indicate whether the verb form is present (**Pr**), past (**Past**), or past participle (**PP**).

a. Anne (*swimming*, *swam*) in the second race. ....

b. Greg and Don have (*decide*, *decided*) to stay for dinner. ....

c. I (*fills*, *filled*) the pool with water last night. ....

d. Jenny and Mark (*draw*, *drawn*) very detailed drawings. ....

Underline the correct form of the irregular verb in the following sentence.

a. She (*sang*, *sung*) beautifully in the recital.

b. The shirt was (*stole*, *stolen*) from the store.

c. The large ship (*sank*, *sunk*) when the torpedo hit it.

d. The bell has (*rang*, *rung*); please go to your class.

e. Martha (*sprang*, *sprung*) forward to catch the little boy who was falling.

Read an article in your local newspaper. Find the answers to the *who*, *what*, *when*, and *where* questions.

Assessment 5

(Lessons 26 - 30)

1. Find and underline three prepositional phrases in the literature passage used in Lesson 16. Circle the object of each preposition.

2. Find and underline two helping verbs in the last paragraph of the literature passage in Lesson 26.

3. Adverbs describe verbs and tell us *how, when, where,* or *to what extent* or *degree.* Write sentences using adverbs illustrating each of these.

4. Find two adverbs in the literature passage in Lesson 5.

5. Write the following dialogue correctly.

   I have been asked to lead the program next week and I am a little nervous. Are you ever afraid to do something new Mark asked. Sometimes replied his father.

BOOK STUDY

on

The Horse and His Boy

Vocabulary

Find each of the following words in the chapters indicated and use context clues to decide the meaning of each word. Then, look up each word in the dictionary and write a definition.

1. jostled - (Chapter 4) _____

   _____

2. queue - /kyoo/ (Chapter 6) _____

   _____

3. council - (Chapter 8) _____

   _____

4. assurance - (Chapter 11) _____

   _____

5. intense - (Chapter 14) _____

   _____

Choose the correct word from the words listed above to complete the following sentences.

6. The theater manager asked the crowd to form a _____ to purchase tickets.

7. The _____ met on Friday night to make a decision.

8. Ryan was _____ in the crowd as he tried to reach his friend.

9. The waiting became _____ as the minutes ticked by.

10. I have the _____ that I will live with God forever.

Discussion Questions

1. Who was your favorite character in this book. Why?

2. What parts made you laugh? Cheer? Afraid for the characters?

3. Were the characters believable? Have you ever known anyone like them?

4. We see pride and humility contrasted in the four main characters. Which were proud? Which were humble? How did this changed by the end of the story?

5. How did you feel about the arranged marriage Aravis' father had planned for her? What did it tell you about her father? Do you think arranged marriages are always wrong?

6. Would you describe Rabadash's punishment as "poetic justice" (getting what he deserved)? Why?

7. Shasta felt that he was a most unfortunate boy; that everything went right for everyone else but him. Have you ever felt like Shasta? When? How did you deal with these feelings?

8. As Shasta walks through the darkness getting colder, feeling alone, and very sorry for himself, he begins to cry. What put a sudden stop to this? What emotions did Shasta experience as he walked though the mist with "The Thing" beside him? As the mist clears, how does Shasta feel?

9. When Aravis exclaims that being in the battle must have been wonderful, Cor replies that it wasn't at all like what he thought. Have you ever experienced anything that turned out to be very different than you thought? Explain.

Activities

The following activities are intended to expand your understanding and enjoyment of this wonderful book. Choose two or three activities of your choice.

1. Since authors always bring part of themselves to their work, it is interesting to find out something about them when you read their books. Find some information about C.S. Lewis and his life.

2. Have you ever ridden a horse? If possible, visit a stable and go for a ride. Do you have to hold on with your knees like Bree told Shasta?

3. The Calormenes are known for their story-telling capabilities. Practice telling an exciting story by choosing an incident from the book, *The Horse and His Boy*.

    Suggestions: Shasta gets separated from the horses and Aravis in Tarkaan
                    the battle scene where Prince Rabadash is defeated

4. *The Horse and His Boy* is a type of literature called *fantasy*. What makes it so?

5. The Calormenes love to quote their poets.

    Example: Natural affection is stronger than soup and offspring more precious than carbuncles.

    This could also be called a proverb. The Bible has a book of Proverbs. Read some and try writing your own proverb.

6. The idea of mistaken identity is intriguing to authors. Some examples are found in books such as Charles Dickens' *The Prince and the Pauper* and Anthony Hope's *The Prisoner of Zenda*. Try writing a story about twins or look-alikes being mistaken for each other.

7. Mr. Lewis uses analogies throughout the Chronicles of Narnia series. An **analogy** is a comparison of two similar things. The main analogy is Aslan as a picture of Jesus. What other analogies did you notice in reading *The Horse and His Boy*?

8. Read the other books in this series:

    The Lion, the Witch, and the Wardrobe
    Prince Caspian
    The Voyage of the Dawn Treader
    The Magician's Nephew
    The Last Battle

I C.A.N. Assessment

for

The Horse and His Boy - Book Study D

After the *Book Study* is completed, check off each I C.A.N. objective with your teacher.

C   I can **complete** my work.

_____   I can be **creative**.

A   I can be **accurate**.

_____   I can do my work with a good **attitude**.

N   I can do my work **neatly**.

Pooh was thoughtful when he heard this, and then he murmured to himself:

But whatever his weight in pounds, shillings, and ounces,
He always seems bigger because of bounces.

"And that's the whole poem," he said. "Do you like it, Piglet?"
"All except the shillings," said Piglet. "I don't think they ought to be there."
"They wanted to come in after the pounds," explained Pooh, "so I let them. It is the best way to write poetry, letting things come."
"Oh, I didn't know," said Piglet.

The House at Pooh Corner by A. A. Milne
© 1956, A.A. Milne

1. a. Read the literature passage. Why do you think the shillings wanted to come into Pooh's poem? Look up *shilling* in the dictionary to find its meaning.

_____

_____

   b. Look at the literature passage paying special attention to punctuation. This literature passage contains written conversation known as dialogue. In what ways does the writer let the reader know a new person is speaking?

_____

_____

   c. Write the literature passage from dictation.

_____

_____

_____

_____

_____

_____

_____

_____

Proofread and correct any mistakes. Make a spelling list of any misspelled words or use the following suggested list:

thoughtful	murmured	weight
pounds	shilling	ounces

d. Look at the words *pounds* and *ounces* in the suggested spelling list. Words with the /ow/ sound are usually spelled with **ow**. Some words are spelled **ou**, but **ou** will usually not end a word.

> **Spelling Tip**
> Most words spell the /ow/ sound
> with **ow**. Some words are
> spelled **ou**.

e. Locate the word in the literature passage with the suffix **-ful**. The suffix **-ful** means *full of*. This suffix usually changes a word into an adjective. Add **-ful** to your suffix list. Also fill in the definition, part of speech, and word examples.

f. Find an adjective in comparative form and an adjective in superlative form in the literature passage. Refer to Lesson 7 if you need any review.

....

g. In the literature passage, what punctuation separates the text from the poem which Pooh composed? .... Why do you think the writer chose this punctuation?

....

2. a. Look at the literature passage. What do you notice about the use of quotation marks? Write two rules about the use of quotation marks.

....

....

....

Refer to the quotation rules in Lesson 7 if you need help.

b. Underline the sentence in the literature passage which contains a split quotation. What special rules apply to a split quotation?

....

....

c. Add correct punctuation to the following direct quotations. Refer to the quotation rules in Lesson 11 if you need help.
    Ex: Come with us to the rally begged Alicia
           "Come with us to the rally," begged Alicia.

    1) We need to find a way for the whole group to take the canoe trip explained Jim

    2) Janice replied I'm not sure I'll be able to afford the cost

    3) One way to help cover the cost interjected Seth is to have a car wash

    4) What a great idea exclaimed Jim That would help reduce everyone's cost.

    5) Where would we have the car wash asked Ruth

Enrichment
Describe a tree.

Describe a bush.

How is a tree like a bush?

How is a tree different from a bush?

What types of offices are there in this country?

What types of stores are there in this country?

How is a store like an office?

How is a store different than an office?

3. a. Dialogue is used in a story to bring the characters to life. Good stories usually contain some element of dialogue. Look through some stories you have available. Do they all contain dialogue?

b. Write a short conversation between you and your teacher. Remember to indent each time you change who is speaking. Be sure to identify the speaker when necessary so the reader is clear about who is speaking.

_____

_____

_____

_____

_____

_____

_____

_____

c. Check your punctuation. Did you use the quotation marks correctly? _____

d. Review your spelling words.

Enrichment

Write two words beginning with each letter for the categories listed.

	L	W	T	S	R
Drinks					
Girl's names					
Verbs					
Cereals					

a. Pooh is very good at making up poetry. The poem he composes in the literature passage is a **couplet**, a two-lined stanza of poetry ending in words that rhyme. What two words in Pooh's poem rhyme? _____

b. In Pooh's poem he is describing his friend, Tigger. Write a list of words that describe someone you know or an animal. Write two or three couplets about this person or animal. Make sure the ending words of each stanza rhyme.

c. Take an oral or written spelling pretest.

5. a. Choose one of the following activities. Complete on separate paper.

   1) Write the literature passage from dictation. Compare your copy with the passage and correct any errors. Were you able to correctly punctuate all the direct quotations?

   2) A play is similar to a short story with dialogue. You can write dialogue in the form of a one-act play. This form of a mini-play is called a **duolog**. Plan your basic plot and decide on your characters. Most stories have a problem of some kind which the characters must overcome. Try to provide the reader with some insight into the personalities of your characters. When writing in play form, quotation marks are not used. When your play is complete, find someone to act it out with you. Look at the following example.

SETTING: A hiking trail that follows a creek in a forest wilderness

NANCY: I don't know how you talked me into this hiking experience. You know how I hate bugs.

JOANNA: Come on Nancy! The bugs aren't that bad. Look at the beauty around you. Enjoy God's wonderful creation.

Review Activities

1. Rewrite the following dialogue adding punctuation.

Do you feel the judging team is ready for the competition asked Martha. I really don't think we are. We need to spend some more time practicing and studying answered Mike. Well, the competition is only two weeks away said Martha and everyone's schedule is full. Then we will have to practice the best we can individually and hope we can still do well as a team at the competition said Mike with a shrug.

_____

_____

_____

_____

_____

_____

_____

2. Write a couplet describing an animal.

_____

_____

_____

_____

_____

_____

Marilla was a tall, thin woman, with angles and without curves; her dark hair showed some gray streaks and was always twisted up in a hard little knot behind with two wire hairpins stuck aggressively through it. She looked like a woman of narrow experience and rigid conscience, which she was; but there was a saving something about her mouth which, if it had been ever so slightly developed, might have been considered indicative of a sense of humour.

Matthew dreaded all women except Marilla and Mrs. Rachel; he had an uncomfortable feeling that the mysterious creatures were secretly laughing at him. He may have been quite right in thinking so, for he was an odd-looking personage, with an ungainly figure and long iron-gray hair that touched his stooping shoulders, and a full, soft brown beard which he had worn ever since he was twenty. In fact, he had looked at twenty very much as he looked at sixty, lacking a little of the grayness.

A child of about eleven, garbed in a very short, very tight, very ugly dress of yellowish gray wincey. She wore a faded brown sailor hat and beneath the hat, extending down her back, were two braids of very thick, decidedly red hair. Her face was small, white and thin, also much freckled; her mouth was large and so were her eyes, that looked green in some lights and moods and gray in others.

Anne of Green Gables by L. M. Montgomery.
Used by permission, David R. Godine Publishers Inc.

1. a. Read the three character descriptions. Can you visualize these people? An author tells about a character by describing him physically, but he also describes his personality. Some description is usually given when a character is first introduced to the reader, as in these paragraphs. This is commonly referred to as a **character sketch**. Look through some books on your shelf and find other character sketches. How does the author make you "see" the person?

   _____

   _____

   b. Write the third paragraph of the literature passage from dictation. Compare your copy with the passage and correct any errors in spelling and punctuation.

   _____

   _____

   _____

Make a spelling list of any misspelled words or use the following suggested list:

garbed   wincey   freckled
decidedly   yellowish   sailor

c. The word *yellowish* contains the suffix **-ish**, meaning *origin, nature*, or *resembling*. Add this to your list of suffixes along with the definition and word examples.

d. Locate the word *uncomfortable* in the literature passage. This word contains the suffix **-able** which means *able* or *can do*. This suffix can also be spelled **-ible** in words such as *invisible* and *sensible*. Add these suffixes to your list along with the definition and word examples.

e. Spelling words with the suffixes **-able** and **-ible** are often confused with one another. Because the suffix **-able** is used more often, the suffix **-ible** is often misspelled. Copy the following words and underline the suffix noting which suffix is used. Say each word aloud as you write them. Listen for the short **/a/** sound or the short **/i/** sound in the suffix.

eligible ....   indispensable ....

legible ....   edible ....

flexible ....   reversible ....

predictable ....   dependable ....

acceptable ....   irritable ....

f. Locate the phrase *with an ungainly figure* in the second paragraph of the literature passage. Why is the article *an* used in this phrase instead of the article *a*? If you are unsure, refer to Lesson 16.

....

....

2. a. An adjective is a word that modifies or describes a noun or pronoun and answers the questions *what kind, how much,* or *which one.* Circle the adjectives in the third paragraph of the literature passage.

b. Look at this simplified sentence from the literature passage.

   Her face was small.

   Adjectives usually come before the noun or pronoun they are describing, but in this sentence the adjective, *small*, comes after the noun, *face*. These are called predicate adjectives. **Predicate adjectives** follow a verb and describes the subject. The verb that links the subject to the predicate adjective is called a **linking verb**.
   Ex: The rising sun is *beautiful*.

   Beautiful is the predicate adjective; it follows the linking verb *is*.

c. Find the predicate adjective in this simplified sentence from the literature passage.

   Her mouth was large.

   What linking verb does it follow? ....
   Draw an arrow from the predicate adjective to the noun or pronoun it describes.

d. Sometimes a noun is described by an adjective of two or more words. When two or more words act together as a single adjective, it is called a **compound adjective.** Sometimes these adjectives are compound words (two words joined together) or hyphenated words.

Find the two compound adjectives in the second paragraph of the literature passage that are joined together by a hyphen.

_____

_____

e. Add hyphens to compound adjectives where needed in the following sentences. Underline any predicate adjectives.

1) She looked beautiful in her floor length dress.
2) The new student was well liked.
3) He had a soft spoken manner and a gentle smile.
4) The theater had a good supply of chocolate covered raisins.
5) The idea you expressed in class was mind boggling.

a. Think of a person you know or create a fictitious character that you would like write to describe in a character sketch. Write down words that you feel would be descriptive of him. Remember, don't just describe the physical features; also describe the person's personality. You can include details about how the person speaks, moves, or dresses. In order to give more insight into his personality you can include details about the person's surroundings, hobbies, plans for the future, viewpoint, and background.

_____

_____

_____

_____

_____

_____

b. Once you have completed your list, write a character sketch about the person you have chosen. Be sure to make use of adjectives in your description. Read the following example of a character sketch.

She looked up expectantly at the entrance way to the college. Her wavy blonde hair encircled her youthful freckled face as her blue eyes glimmered with the spark of determination. A faded flowered dress caressed her slender frame in the breeze as she stood momentarily with her one suitcase of possessions. She knew she must succeed; she had worked too hard for this day.

c. Review your spelling words.

Enrichment

Use an atlas or map to make an alphabet trip across North America. Begin in a city that begins with the letter **A**. Write the name of the city on the map. Then travel to a city that begins with the letter **C** and mark your path from **A** to city **C**. Continue with the letters **Across America**.

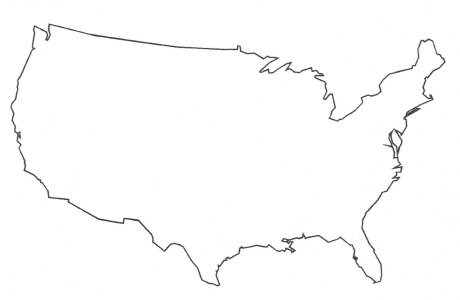

a. To tell the difference between an adjective and an adverb, remember that an adjective always describes a noun or pronoun. An adverb can describe a verb, adjective, or another adverb. It answers the questions *how, where, how often, when,* and *to what extent.* When an adverb describes an adjective it usually appears just before the adjective and tells *how* or *to what extent.* If the adverb is describing an adverb, it usually appears just before the adverb and usually tells *how.*

b. List the six adverbs found in the third paragraph of the literature passage. One adverb is used four times. Beside each adverb listed, write the word it describes and indicate whether it is describing a verb, adjective, or another adverb.

c. Look up the word *garbed* in the dictionary to find the definition. Use the word correctly in a sentence.

d. Take an oral or written spelling pretest.

An Enrichment Activity is on the next page.

Enrichment
Read each sentence below. One word in each sentence is a made up word. Decide what part of speech that word is in the sentence. Write your answer in the blank.

noun   verb   adjective   adverb

1) The green klumper was late. klumper is a _____

2) Mary ran home frumperly. frumperly is a _____

3) The glutterton whale is huge. glutterton is a _____

4) Tommy kapluckered home. kapluckered is a _____

5) The pig went fusa up the hill. fusa is a _____

6) The bevish lady blattered down the street. bevish is a _____

   blattered is a _____

7) The little wersala climbed hetterly up the tree. wersala is a _____

   hetterly is a _____

BONUS:

8) The whatson pearleton fittered meraly. whatson is a _____

   pearleton is a _____ fittered is a _____

   meraly is a _____

5. a. Choose one of the following activities. Complete on separate paper.

   1) Write the third paragraph of the literature passage from dictation. Correct any errors in spelling and punctuation.

   2) Using the three descriptive paragraphs of the literature passage, draw a picture of one or more of the characters. Pay attention to details.

   3) Choose skills from the *Review Activities* on the next page.

Review Activities

1. Add suffixes from your list that match the definition of the following words.

   a. fool + (*having the nature of a fool*) = ...

   b. sneak + (*inclined to sneak*) = ...

   c. like + (*able to like*) = ...

   d. life + (*without life*) = ...

2. Underline the adjectives and circle the adverbs in the following sentences. Draw an arrow to the word each is modifying.

   a. The sun rose quickly over the steep mountaintops and chased the dark shadows from the lush meadows.

   b. The fierce waves break against the rugged shore before the storm.

   c. The very agitated boy struck the hard ground with his small fist.

   d. Yesterday we decided we can never know which team will win the game.

   e. The orange frisbee was expertly caught by the clever dog as the wide-eyed group of children watched.

The Crow and the Pitcher

A crow perishing with thirst saw a pitcher, and hoping to find water, flew to it with delight. When he reached it, he discovered to his grief that it contained so little water that he could not possibly get at it. He tried everything he could think of to reach the water, but all his efforts were in vain. At last he collected as many stones as he could carry and dropped them one by one with his beak into the pitcher, until he brought the water within his reach and thus saved his life.

Aesop's Fables

1. a. Before writing this literature passage, look at the title. Why are certain words in the title capitalized and others not?

   _____

   Write the literature passage from dictation, then compare with the model. Correct any errors you find.

b. Make a list of any misspelled words or use the following suggested spelling list:

perishing	delight	discovered
possibly	contained	grief

c. What spelling rule will help you remember how to spell *grief*?

d. Look at the word *discovered* from your suggested spelling list. Note how the suffix **-ed** is added to the word. The last consonant, **r**, is not doubled because it is preceded by a vowel.

> ### Spelling Tip
> Words with more than one syllable that end with a consonant preceded by a vowel do not double the final consonant when adding a suffix beginning with a vowel unless the last syllable is accented.

Ex: travel - traveled (The last syllable is not accented.)
       commit - committed (The last syllable is accented.)

e. Add suffixes to the following words applying this *Spelling Tip*. Also remember that one-syllable words ending with the one vowel and one consonant doubles the last consonant before adding a suffix beginning with a vowel.

1) begin + ing _____

2) refer + ed _____

3) recoil + ed _____

4) admit + ing _____

5) trap + ed _____

6) benefit + ed _____

7) ship + ing _____

8) marvel + ed _____

9) transfer + ing _____

10) shop + ing _____

f. The suggested spelling list contains the prefixes **dis-**, **con-**, and **de-**. Refer to your list of prefixes for the meaning of each. Use the correct prefix to complete each of the following words.

1) The members of the club _____verged on the small town for the annual meeting. (*together, with*)
2) I am afraid Mary has become _____couraged after she did poorly on the test. (*take away*)
3) The team will _____part at 2:00 P.M. in order to be on time for the track meet. (*down, from*)

g. How does the crow in the literature passage exhibit the character quality of resourcefulness?

_____

_____

_____

_____

2. a. Look at the simplified sentence from the literature passage, and underline the subject and circle the verb.

    A crow saw a pitcher.

b. Now ask the question "A crow saw what?" Circle the noun that answers that question. The noun you circled is called the **direct object**. Direct objects receive the action from the verb and answer the questions *what* or *whom* after an action verb. A direct object must be a noun or pronoun.

Look at the following examples. Find the verb and ask the questions *what* or *whom*.

The boy threw the ball. (Threw what? *Ball* is the direct object.)
Mom baked a cake. (Baked what? *Cake* is the direct object.)
Ginger held it tightly. (Held what? *It* is the direct object.)

c. A sentence may have more than one direct object. Sometimes you have a compound direct object.
    Ex: Dan chose Mike and Lisa to be on his team.
          (Chose whom? *Mike* and *Lisa* are the direct objects.)

d. A direct object is never part of a prepositional phrase.
   Ex: David lifted the rock over his head.
         (Rock is the direct object. *Over his head* is a prepositional phrase. *Head* is the
         object of the preposition, *over*.)

e. Underline the action verbs in the last sentence of the literature passage.

f. Read the action verbs you have underlined and ask the question "What?" If there is a
   noun or pronoun that answers the question, circle it. Not all action verbs have a direct
   object.
   Ex: collected what?

g. Underline the action verbs and circle the direct objects in the following sentences.

   1) The pilot flew his plane into enemy territory.

   2) The horse jumped the fence.

   3) Jenny baked chocolate chip cookies and peanut butter candies for the party.

   4) The Pilgrims signed the Mayflower Compact before leaving the ship.

   5) Galileo developed a working telescope.

a. *Aesop's Fables* were written to teach lessons or morals.   What do you think is the moral
   of this fable?

   ....

   ....

b. Try an experiment filling a cup half full of water. Drop pebbles or marbles into the cup.
   What happens to the water level?

   ....

c. Read the following two morals which Aesop wrote about.

   Whatever you do, do with all your might.
   Those who seek to please everybody please nobody.

   List three other morals that could be written as a fable. If you have trouble thinking of
   three, read over the book of Proverbs in the Bible for ideas.

   ....

   ....

d. Review your spelling words.

Enrichment
Write a sentence using:

aderfee as an adjective

_____

budenforf as a noun

_____

citedly as an adverb

_____

rufont as a noun

_____

4. a. Choose one of the morals you listed in **3c** and write a fable about it. Fables usually use animals that talk and act like human beings. They are simply written, usually involving only two or three characters. One character faces a problem or situation and tries to overcome it. The ending will always teach us a lesson, or moral.

_____

_____

_____

_____

_____

_____

_____

_____

b. Take an oral or written spelling pretest.

Enrichment

Write two words beginning with each letter for each category.

	B	G	K	W	S
Land Animal					
Insect					
Sea Animal					
Clothes					

a. Choose one of the following activities. Complete on separate paper.

1) Rewrite the literature passage from dictation.

2) Read about the history of *Aesop's Fables* in a reference book or read two or three fables and explain their morals.

3) Choose skills from the *Review Activities* on the next page.

Review Activities

1. Underline the action verbs and circle the direct objects in the following sentences.

    a. At night many bats eat insects which they locate with their high-pitched radar.

    b. Spiders capture moths and flies in their intricate webs.

    c. In early hours of dusk dragonflies chase mosquitoes throughout the sky.

    d. Birds devour many insects during the daytime hours.

    e. Insects encounter many enemies everyday.

2. Write a fable that depicts a moral message.

Laurie had vanished round the bend, Jo was just at the turn, and Amy, far behind, striking out toward the smoother ice in the middle of the river. For a minute Jo stood still with a strange feeling at her heart; then she resolved to go on, but something held and turned her round, just in time to see Amy throw up her hands and go down, with the sudden crash of rotten ice, the splash of water, and a cry that made Jo's heart stand still with fear.

Little Women by Louisa May Alcott

a. Read the literature passage. Write it from dictation. Compare your copy to the passage. Did you place the commas in the right places?

b. Make a spelling list from any misspelled words from your dictation or use the following suggested list:

vanished	smoother	strange
resolved	sudden	rotten

Divide the words into syllables. This will help you remember the spelling. What do you notice about the division of syllables in the words *sudden* and *rotten*?

c. Divide the following words into syllables.
Ex: supper - sup/per

1) butter _____   4) invite _____

2) master _____   5) cotton _____

3) fiddle _____

d. To form the plural of words ending in **o**, first look at the word. If the **o** is preceded by a consonant, add **es**; otherwise, just add **s**. Music related words are exceptions; just add **s** regardless of how the word ends.
Ex: hero - heroes (**o** preceded by a consonant)
     banjo - banjos (music related word)
     studio - studios (**o** preceded by a vowel)

Spelling Tip
To form the plural of words ending in **o** preceded by a consonant, add **es**; otherwise, just add **s**. **Exception:** Music related words - just add **s**.

e. Write the following words in plural form.

1) piano _____   4) alto _____

2) tomato _____   5) potato _____

3) video _____

a. Find the adjective *smoother* in the literature passage. Is *smoother* a positive, comparative, or superlative adjective? If you are not sure, refer to Lesson 7. What things are being compared?

....

....

b. Find the possessive noun in the literature passage. What punctuation identifies the word as a possessive noun? .... What object does the possessive noun own? ....

c. Possessive pronouns such as *her, his, my, our*, and *their* show ownership without the use of an apostrophe and **s**. Circle the possessive pronouns in the literature passage. Substitute a possessive noun for each of the possessive pronouns. Read the literature passage with the substitutions. Which version sounds better? ....

   Laurie had vanished round the bend, Jo was just at the turn, and Amy, far behind, striking out toward the smoother ice in the middle of the river. For a minute Jo stood still with a strange feeling at Jo's heart; then Jo resolved to go on, but something held and turned Jo around, just in time to see Amy throw up Amy's hands and go down, with the sudden crash of rotten ice, the splash of water, and a cry that made Jo's heart stand still with fear.

d. Who are the characters in the passage?

....

Imagine Amy is your sister and you are at the scene depicted in the literature passage. Write a few sentences explaining what you think may have happened next in the story. Choose descriptive adjectives to express how you feel.

....

....

....

....

3. a. A **semicolon** separates two independent clauses that are joined together without a conjunction. Circle the semicolon (;) and underline the two independent clauses in the following simplified sentence.

   For a minute Jo stood still with a strange feeling at her heart; then she resolved to go on.

   b. Look at this simplified sentence from the literature passage.

   She resolved to go on, but something held and turned her round.

   A comma is used before the conjunction because it joins two complete sentences. This is called a **compound sentence**.

   Rewrite the following sentences as compound sentences by using the conjunctions *and*, *but*, or *or*. Remember the comma.

   1) Jason plays baseball. Lynn plays basketball.

   _____

   _____

   2) Sue likes ice cream. I like frozen yogurt.

   _____

   _____

   3) We tried to be on time. We were late.

   _____

   _____

   c. Review your spelling words. Be sure to sound them out by syllables as you write them.

   Enrichment
   Read the following sentences one time. Then close the book and draw a picture on a separate sheet of paper of what you read. Reread the sentences to check your picture.

   The two boys were playing in the backyard all day. They each had two trucks and a shovel. They made roads in the sand for their trucks. They made high hills, too. It looked like fun.

a. Find and circle the action verbs in the paragraph. You learned in Lesson 29 that verbs change their form in order to show the time of an action. These forms of verbs are called **tenses**. A verb may be written in present, past, or future tense (time). In what tense is the literature passage written? _____

b. The literature passage was written by the author in past tense. Rewrite the literature passage as if you were Jo telling it as it is happening. (first person, present tense).
Ex: Laurie vanishes round the bend, I am just at the turn, and Amy, far behind, is striking out toward the smoother ice in the middle of the river...

c. Take a practice test of your spelling words.

_____

_____

_____

5. a. Choose one of the following activities. Complete on separate paper.

   1) Write the literature passage once again from dictation. Pay close attention to your punctuation and spelling.

   2) Write a short story describing an exciting event in your life.

   3) Choose skills from the *Review Activities* on the next page.

Review Activities

1. Divide the following words into syllables:

a. riddle _____   d. blanket _____

b. tablet _____   e. bottom _____

c. confess _____   f. hobby _____

2. Circle the correct spelling of the following words.

a. echos, echoes   d. cellos, celloes

b. tornados, tornadoes   e. stereos, stereoes

c. sopranos, sopranoes   f. potatos, potatoes

3. Underline the possessive nouns in the following sentences and change them to possessive pronouns.
Ex: Please turn down the volume on <u>Mike's</u> radio. ___his___

a. We will be attending Laurie's graduation ceremony. _____

b. Lane's fishing spot is the best one on the lake. _____

c. Will the youth group's skit be done soon? _____

d. Did you know the Smith family's vacation was canceled? _____

e. Anne's horse completed all the jumps. _____

4. Write the past tense form of the following verbs.

a. freeze _____   d. catch _____

b. spring _____   e. twirl _____

c. splash _____   f. weep _____

5. Find a paragraph in a book. Change the tense to past or present.

Here Louisa played on the grass, made friends with the passersby, or, plumping down to rest, would sit looking up at the tall elms with their high trunks and enormously long branches, so different from the round leafy beeches of the woods at her birthplace. The tall elderly houses of Beacon Hill looked down on her out of their many-paned windows, where the blue and purple glass was a sign of exceedingly aristocratic old age.

1. a. Write the literature passage from dictation. Compare your copy to the passage and correct any errors.

b. Look up the word *aristocratic* in the dictionary. What does it mean?

c. Make a spelling list of any misspelled words from your dictation or use the following suggested list:

passersby	enormously	birthplace
elderly	aristocratic	exceedingly

d. Three of the words in the suggested spelling list have the same suffix. Identify the suffix. What part of speech are each of these words? Remember, most words ending in **-ly** are adverbs. Some are adjectives, such as *friendly* and *lovely.*

e. What two words in the suggested spelling list are compound words? _____

What words make up each compound? _____

f. Find the word *different* in the literature passage. Usually words ending in **-ent** and **-ant** sound alike but are often misspelled. It is the same with words ending in **-ence** and **-ance**. When spelling a word with one of these endings, carefully enunciate each syllable.

Spelling Tip
Do not confuse the spelling of words ending in **-ent** and **-ence** with words ending in **-ant** and **-ance.**

g. Copy the following words under the correct heading.

defiant	defiance	confidence
confident	instant	instance
dependence	dependent	insistent
insistence	relevant	relevance
resistant	resistance	abundant
abundance	sentence	persistent
persistence	existence	insolent

-ant	**-ent**	**-ance**	**-ence**
defiant	confident	instance	independence

2. a. Find the word *beech* in the literature passage. What is the meaning of this word?

_____ Can you think of a homonym for the word *beech*? _____

What is the meaning of the homonym? _____

b. The first word of the literature passage is *here;* it is telling us where Louisa played. Words that answer the questions *where, how, when,* or *how much* are called adverbs.

c. Adverbs modify or describe verbs, but they also can describe adjectives or another adverb. Look at the phrase *enormously long branches*. What is the noun being

described? _____ What word describes the branches? _____

What word describes *long*? _____

d. Look at the last phrase of the literature passage.

　　of exceedingly aristocratic old age

Underline the adjective and circle the adverb.

e. A good writer uses strong verbs and descriptive adverbs and adjectives to help the reader see and feel what is happening. Sometimes, a writer will give human qualities to animals or objects to bring the story alive. This is called **personification**.
Ex: Bright yellow daisies peeked over the hillside.
Daisies do not really peek, but with the use of personification, the daisies come alive.

Find an example of personification in the literature passage.

_____

_____

f. Write a paragraph that tells about your home or neighborhood. Be sure to use descriptive adjectives and adverbs.

_____

_____

_____

_____

_____

_____

_____

3. a. A **biography** is a nonfiction story of a person's life written by someone else. Biographies contain information about a person's life such as when they were born, their childhood, their interests, and more. Think of someone you know that you think would be interesting to interview; perhaps a grandparent, a missionary friend, or someone who has achieved goals you would also like to achieve. Make a list of questions you would like to ask him. Then ask permission for an interview and schedule an appointment. Be sure to take along a camera and take a picture if possible. Complete on a separate sheet of paper.

b. Below are some sample questions that could be used for the interview.

Sample Interview Questions

1) When and where were you born?
2) What did your parents do for a living?
3) Where did you grow up?
4) Where did you go to school?
5) What are some of your fondest childhood memories?
6) How many brothers and sisters did you have?
7) Where did you go to church?
8) What were your interests growing up?
9) What kind of jobs did you work as a teenager?
10) Did you go to college? If so, where?
11) Where you ever in the military?
12) What kind of job did you start with after finishing school?
13) Where did you first meet your husband/wife?
14) What attracted you to him/her?
15) When did you get married?
16) Where did you first live after getting married?
17) How many children did you have?
18) What was your family like?
19) What goals have you had in your life and have you reached them?
20) What is the most important advice you could give me?

---

c. Review your spelling words.

a. Interview the person using the questions as a guideline. Ask the person if you may use a tape recorder to record the interview. Take careful notes of what they say. Complete on a separate sheet of paper.

b. Compare the recorded interview with your notes. Did you miss anything important?

c. Begin your biography by following these guidelines.

1) Read through your notes and determine the main idea.
2) Decide on your opening sentence. Try to capture your audience's attention by presenting your topic in an interesting way.
3) Biographies are usually written in chronological order, so write your sentences accordingly.

d. Take an oral or written spelling pretest.

Enrichment
Use colored paper to make the following:

1. a red circle on a yellow square on a green triangle
2. a green square on a blue circle on a red triangle
3. a blue triangle on a green triangle on a yellow circle
4. a green rectangle on a red square on a blue circle

5. a. Choose one of the following activities. Complete on separate sheet of paper.

   1) Write the literature passage from dictation. Check your copy for spelling and punctuation.

   2) Complete writing the biography. Edit carefully for mistakes and make a final copy for your teacher. If possible include a picture of the person you interviewed.

   3) Choose skills from the *Review Activities* on the next page.

Review Activities

1. Circle the adjectives and underline the adverbs in the following paragraph.

The sun shone brillantly in the clear blue sky. Majestic oaks gently spread their strong limbs to shade the little creatures from the scorching sun. The babbling brook gingerly wound its way through the tiny crevices in the rocky hillside. The quiet woodlands patiently waited for the coolness of dusk.

2. Find one example of personification in the paragraph above.

_____

_____

3. Read a short biography of a famous person. Compare the biography you wrote in Lesson 35 with the one you read. Does it contain some of the same elements? Is there anything you would like to add to your next biography?

_____

_____

_____

_____

_____

_____

_____

_____

_____

_____

You are the salt of the earth; but if the salt has become tasteless, how will it be made salty again? It is good for nothing anymore, except to be thrown out and trampled under foot by men. You are the light of the world. A city set on a hill cannot be hidden. Nor do men light a lamp and put it under the peck measure, but on the lampstand; and it gives light to all who are in the house. Let your light shine before men in such a way that they may see your good works, and glorify your Father who is in heaven.

Matthew 5:13-16 (NASB)

1. a. Read the literature passage. Write it from dictation.

_____

_____

_____

_____

_____

_____

_____

_____

_____

_____

_____

_____

_____

_____

_____

Compare your copy with the passage and correct all spelling and punctuation errors. Why is the word *Father* capitalized?

b. What is the suffix in the word *tasteless*? _____ How does this suffix change the meaning of the root word *taste*? _____

c. The suffix **-fy** appears in the word *glorify* in the literature passage. This suffix means *make*. Add it to your list of suffixes. Can you think of any other words that have this suffix? How was the spelling of the root word *glory* changed before this suffix was added?

d. Make a spelling list of any misspelled words or use the following suggested list:

tasteless	trampled	lampstand
measure	glorify	works

_____

_____

_____

e. Find two verbs from the suggested spelling list that is written in the past tense. Are they regular verbs (**R**) or irregular verbs (**IR**)?

f. Look at the word *works* from the suggested spelling list. When spelling a word with a /w/ sound followed by the /er/ sound, the word is usually spelled **wor**.

Spelling Tip
Words like **works** with the
/wer/ sound are usually
spelled **wor**.

g. Copy these words and underline **wor**. Say the words aloud as you write them.

word _____   worth _____   world _____

worm _____   worse _____   worry _____

a. In what person is the literature passage written? First, second, or third? _____ What pronoun used throughout the literature passage helps you determine in what person the passage is written? _____

b. Look up the word *glorify* in the dictionary. What does it mean?

_____

How can God be glorified by your good works? _____

_____

Memorize the last sentence of the literature passage. Practice until you can say it and write it from memory.

c. Read the first sentence of the literature passage again. It compares *you* with *salt*. When a comparison of two unlike things is made <u>without</u> using *like* or *as* it is called a **metaphor**. Find another metaphor in the literature passage. Tell your teacher what two things are being compared.

_____

d. Write two metaphors. Be sure not to use *like* or *as* in your comparison.
   Ex: This situation is a thorn in my side.

_____

_____

_____

Enrichment
Use a clock or watch to see how long it takes you to do the following:

Say the alphabet backwards. _____

Flip two coins and get the same side 10 times. _____

Find the word *juggle* in the dictionary. _____

Count from 5 to 200 by fives. _____

Write your name backwards.

a. Find some information about salt and light in an encyclopedia, science book, or library book. What are some uses for salt and light? What are some of their characteristics? Write down what you find.

_____

_____

_____

_____

b. The literature passage is filled with comparisons. One way to compare words is to look at a word that means the opposite of the word. This is the **antonym** of the word. For example, the antonym of *light* is *dark*.

c. Choose the word from the word group that is the best antonym for each word.

1) tall	little, small, short
2) slow	fast, accelerate, sluggish
3) sunny	windy, hot, cloudy
4) loud	shrill, quiet, peaceful
5) near	beside, removed, far

Enrichment

a. Karen runs the mile in 7 minutes.
b. Jason runs the mile slower than Karen.
c. Kelly runs the mile thirty seconds slower than Jason.
d. Matt runs the mile thirty seconds faster than Karen, but one minute faster than Jason.
e. Who runs the mile in 8 minutes? _____

a. Find the word *cannot* in the literature passage. The word *cannot* contains the negative word *not*. Do not use two negative words in the same sentence. Some negative words are *no, not, (n't), nothing, none, never, no one, hardly,* and *scarcely.*
Ex: I *don't hardly* ever go there.
     (Incorrect - contains two negative words.)

     I *don't* ever go there. (Correct)
     I *hardly* ever go there. (Correct)

b. Choose the correct word. Avoid double negatives.
   Ex: We couldn't see (*anything*, *nothing*) in the darkness.

   1) I don't (*never*, *ever*) run in the hallway.

   2) We couldn't see (*any*, *none*) of the boats that were crossing the river.

   3) She didn't receive (*any*, *no*) donations for the mission fund.

   4) I never found (*anything*, *nothing*) in the refrigerator to snack on.

   5) We (*can*, *cannot*) scarcely do anything without someone changing the plans.

c. In the verses that make up the literature passage Jesus says that His followers are like salt
   and light. What do you think Jesus is encouraging us to do? Write a paragraph
   explaining how people can be salt and light. Use the information you found in your
   research in **3a** to help you.

   _____

   _____

   _____

   _____

   _____

   _____

   _____

   _____

d. Take an oral or written spelling pretest.

   _____

   _____

   _____

5. a. Choose one of the following activities. Complete on separate sheet of paper.

   1) Write the literature passage from dictation. Be sure to correct any spelling errors.

   2) Write a thank you note to someone who has been a *light* in your life.

   3) Choose skills from the *Review Activities* on the next page.

Review Activities

1. Knowing that the suffix **-fy** means *to make*, try to define the following words. Then look them up in the dictionary to see if you are correct.

a. liquefy _____

b. fortify _____

c. simplify _____

2. Underline the metaphors in the following paragraph. There is also one simile contained in the paragraph. Identify the simile and be sure not to confuse it with the metaphors.

   The sound of her voice was a summer breeze that brought warmth to everything it touched. Her eyes were blue sapphires that sparkled from under thick, long lashes and glowed with happy thoughts. Her laugh was like a thousand tinkling bells awakening the world with a cheerful sound.

3. Write an antonym for each of the following words. If you have trouble thinking of an antonym, use a thesaurus. Antonyms are usually listed at the end of the list of synonyms.

a. divide _____

b. guilty _____

c. eagerly _____

d. trust _____

e. fact _____

4. Rewrite the following paragraph correcting any double negatives.

We don't hardly ever go to the store without first making a list of the items we need to purchase. I cannot scarcely understand how anyone remembers everything they need without making a list. Mary didn't need no help in getting all the necessary items together at the store, and I didn't find nothing missing when we arrived home.

Assessment 6
(Lessons 31 - 36)

1. Write three sentences describing yourself. Circle the adjectives you used.

2. Adjectives describe nouns answering the questions *what kind, how much,* or *which ones.* Write three sentences using adjectives that answer each of these questions.

3. Write the title of a book you've read.

4. How are adjectives and different?

5. Circle the direct object in the following sentence.

   Sharon played the piano beautifully.

6. Circle the pronouns in the literature passage used in Lesson 34. Tell what the antecedent of each pronoun is.

7. Look at the first three sentences in the literature passage in Lesson 16. Make a list of the verbs. Write the verbs under the correct column below.

Present Tense   **Past Tense**

8. Looking at your list of verbs from the question above, which of them are regular verbs (**R**)? Which are irregular (**IR**)? Note your answers on the chart above.

9. What is a biography?

10. Read the following sentences and write **CS** if it is a complete sentence or **F** if it is a fragment.

   a. I was tired after running the race. ＿＿＿＿＿＿＿

   b. Gloria's sweet face. ＿＿＿＿＿＿＿

   c. The walls were painted blue. ＿＿＿＿＿＿＿

   d. Very fast moving ship. ＿＿＿＿＿＿＿

   e. Running the race. ＿＿＿＿＿＿＿

Commonly Used Prefixes

A prefix is a letter or group of letters which come before the base or root word, changing the meaning of the word.

a, an - not, without (*anonymous, apathy*)
ab - away, from (*abomination, absent, absolve*)
al - to or towards (*alarm, alcove*)
ante - before (*antecedent, antemeridian*)
anti - against (*antibiotic, anticlimactic, antifreeze*)
be - on, away (*beguile, behind, betray*)
bene - well (*benediction, benevolence, beneficiary*)
bi - both (*biathlon, biannual, bicycle*)
bio - living (*biology, biopsy, biography*)
by - near, side (*bylaw, bygone, bystander*)
circ - around (*circumstance, circumstantial, circulation*)
co, con - together, with (*cohabitant, coheir, copilot*)
contra - against (*contraband, contradict, contrary*)
de - down, from (*deprivation, depression, denounce*)
di - twice, two (*diameter, dialect, dialogue*)
dis - reverse, apart, take away (*disarray, disappoint, disintegrate*)
dys - bad (*dyspepsia, dystrophy, dyslexia*)
en - in, into (*envelope, endow, enforce*)
ex - out (*extol, excitement, exchange*)
extra - beyond (*extracurricular, extraneous, extragalactic*)
fore - before in time (*forego, foremost, forefather*)
il, im, in - into - (*illuminate, implant, inside*)
il, im, in, ir - not (*illegal, impartial, indivisible, irrelevant*)
inter - between (*intermission, interrupt, intercept*)
mal - poorly, badly (*malady, malpractice, maladjusted*)
mis - incorrect (*misspell, misinterpret, misconduct*)
mono - one (*monogamous, monotone, monocle*)
multi - many (*multiplication, multipurpose, multitude*)
neo - new (*neolithic, neonatal, neophyte*)
non - not (*nonfiction, nonsense, nonexistent*)
para - almost, beside (*paragraph, paraphrase, parachute*)
per - complete, through (*perambulate, perceptible, percolator*)
poly - many (*polygamy, polyunsaturated, polyurethane*)
post - after (*postwar, postgraduate, postglacial*)
pre - before (*preview, prevent, precursor*)
pro - in favor of, forward (*pro-life, prolific, prologue*)
pseudo - false (*pseudonym, pseudoclassic*)
quad - four (*quadruplets, quadrant, quadriplegic*)
quint - five (*quintuplets, quintet, quintile*)
re - back, again (*return, remember, revive*)
retro - backwards (*retrospect, retroactive*)
self - by oneself (*self-serve, self-indulgent, self-employed*)
sub - under (*submarine, subway, substitute*)
super - over, more (*superhuman, supernatural, supervise*)
trans - across (*transcontinental, translate, transfusion*)
tri - three (*tricycle, tripod, trimester*)
ultra - beyond (*ultraviolet, ultramodern, ultraconservative*)
un - not, release (*undress, untie, undo*)
under - beneath (*underline, underground*)
uni - one (*universe, unity, unicycle*)

Commonly Used Suffixes

A suffix is a letter or group of letters which come after the base or root word, changing the meaning of the word. The suffix is usually helpful in determining the part of speech (noun, verb, adjective, etc.).

able, ible - able to do (*sensible, possible, pliable*)
age - act or state of (*manage, salvage, bandage*)
al - relating to (*final, natural, remedial*)
an, ian, ese, ish - native of (*American, Japanese, Spanish*)
ance, ence - action, state of (*abstinence, reluctance, alliance*)
ant - agent, performing (*reactant, servant*)
ar, er, or - one who, that which (*operator, manager, beggar*)
ary, ery, ory - relating to, connected with, place where (*category, supervisory, infirmary, stationery*)
asis - process, condition (*hypothesis, neurosis, carthasis*)
ate - make, cause (*compassionate, suffocate, generate*)
cian - having a certain skill (*physician, musician, technician*)
cide - kill (*infanticide, suicide, homicide*)
cule - very small (*minuscule, molecule, ridicule*)
cy - action, function (*vagrancy, truancy, leniency*)
dom - quality, realm, office (*freedom, wisdom, kingdom*)
ee - one who receives the action (*emcee, employee, refugee*)
en - make, made of (*flatten, lighten, wooden*)
er - one who or that which - (*singer, mocker*)
ess - female (*princess, goddess, actress*)
et, ette - group, a small one (*majorette, midget*)
ful - full of (*beautiful, joyful, plentiful*)
fy - make (*multiply, unify, amplify*)
hood - condition, order, quality (*neighborhood, brotherhood, womanhood*)
ic - nature of, like (*fantastic, poetic, heroic*)
ice - condition, state (*justice, poultice, novice*)
ile - relating to, capable of (*senile, revile, penile*)
ine - nature of (*clandestine, morphine, chlorine*)
ion, sion, tion - act of, state of, result of (*intrusion, salutation, opinion*)
ish - origin, resembling (*childish, fiendish, reddish*)
ism - system, characteristic (*Buddhism, Communism, monotheism*)
ist - one who, that which (*pianist, philanthropist, dentist*)
ite - nature or quality of (*stalagmite, infinite*)
ity, ty - state or quality of (*university, clarity, unity*)
ive - causing, making (*captive, active, submissive*)
ize - make (*victimize, scrutinize, penalize*)
less - without (*thoughtless, helpless, homeless*)
ly - like, manner of (*lovely, quickly, softly*)
ment - act or state of (*bewilderment, sentiment, advertisement*)
ness - state of (*happiness, holiness, sleeplessness*)
oid - like (*android, spheroid, steroid*)
ology - study, science (*theology, sociology, biology*)
ous, ious, eous - full of, having (*spacious, superfluous, fabulous*)
ship - office, state, quality (*fellowship, friendship*)
sis - process, condition (*hypothesis, neurosis, catharsis*)
some - like, tending to (*meddlesome, twosome, lonesome*)
tude - state or condition of (*solitude, altitude, multitude*)
ure - state of, act, rank (*seizure, rapture, culture*)
ward - in the direction of (*forward, backward, wayward*)
y - inclined to, tend to (*bumpy, silky, scary*)

www.commonsensepress.com

Congratulations,

You Are Part Of The *Common Sense Press* Family.

Now you can receive our FREE e-mail newsletter, containing:
- Teaching Tips
- Product Announcements
- Helpful Hints from Veteran Homeschoolers
- & Much More!

*Please take a moment to register with us
by photocopying or tearing out this page and mailing it to:*

Common Sense Press
Product Registration
8786 Highway 21
Melrose, FL 32666

Or better yet, register online at
www.commonsensepress.com/register

After registering, search our site for teaching tips, product information,
and ways to get more from your *Common Sense Press* purchase.

Your Name _____

Your E-Mail Address _____

Your Address _____

City _____ State _____ Zip _____

Product Purchased _____

From What Company Did You Purchase This Product? _____

Get involved with the *Common Sense Press* community.
Visit our web site often to contribute your ideas, read what others
are doing teaching their children, see new teaching tips, and more.